The Open Heart

by

N. Amosoff

Translated from the Russian
by George St. George

Simon and Schuster · New York

PUBLISHED BY SIMON AND SCHUSTER
ROCKEFELLER CENTER, 630 FIFTH AVENUE
NEW YORK, NEW YORK 10020

FIRST PRINTING

LIBRARY OF CONGRESS CATALOG CARD NUMBER: 67-10898
DESIGNED BY EVE METZ
MANUFACTURED IN THE UNITED STATES OF AMERICA
AMERICAN BOOK–STRATFORD PRESS, INC.

INTRODUCTION

There are days in every man's life which stand out in his memory, which time cannot erase. There are many days, happy days, sad, even tragic, but time usually buries them all under the heaps of other days, and they cease to be remembered.

One of the unforgettable days occurred some years ago, and that was the day on which I started my diary. Or rather I wrote my first entry on the morning that followed it, and then abandoned the book for a long time.

Then there was another day, about two years later, I don't know exactly because I did not date either entry, and then I wrote again, and then I stopped again.

So there are just two entries in my diary, if one can call it a diary, and I like to call them The First Day and The Second Day, because I know that no matter how long I live these two days will stay with me till the day I die.

The First Day

1

TAMARA

THE MORGUE. Such an inoffensive little building standing in the depth of our Institute garden. It is pleasant here. The bright green of the trees. Flowers. It seems that Red Riding Hood should be using this path. No. Here they carry corpses.

I am a doctor. I am going to an autopsy. Yesterday a little girl died during an operation. She had a complicated congenital heart condition, and we operated, disconnecting her heart and using our artificial-blood-circulation machine. This is a new technique. Newspapermen describe it rhapsodically: A dying child . . . the heart is switched off . . . the machine takes over . . . some ten, twenty, thirty minutes . . . a heroic struggle . . . sweat on the surgeon's brow . . . All is well! The surgeon, exhausted but happy, tells the waiting parents that their child is saved. In two weeks the boy is playing football.

They can all go to hell.

I am going to perform an autopsy. No doctor likes this procedure, finishing his work in the morgue. I don't like it either. When there are simple cases, I send my interns to do it. Later on they report to me during our usual morning conferences. A few terse words, some complicated medical terms (young interns like to sound scientific), and a human being is written off. At least, that is how it would sound to anyone listening to their words: ". . . the autopsy has produced the following conclusive findings." Simple? No, not simple at all. All those cut-up corpses live in my memory, there is hardly any room left there for more. I am choking on them.

Stop, Professor! Don't start feeling sorry for yourself again. Go and do your work. Your day is just beginning.

Our morgue is like all morgues, sort of gray. The windows are wide enough, but somehow only a little light filters through. And not only because they are covered halfway up with thin white paint. I don't know why.

A zinc-covered table. Poverty. It should have been marble. However, to a corpse it makes no difference. It is funny, I have seen so many of them, but I still can't get used to them. There she lies, such a tiny, thin body upon such a big, cold table. Two pigtails. Her mother probably braided them for the last time yesterday morning. The pink ribbons are crumpled. It is best not to look. But no, I must. This is my handiwork.

"Let's start."

The dissecting-room people are probably used to this. They don't treat people, just cut them up. But perhaps they also have some feelings. I must give them this credit.

Our doctors are here. Some of them were helping me yesterday. They seem to be depressed enough. I get so angry when they laugh in the dissecting room. Here is death, take off your hats! But, of course, all that is comparative.

I must determine now whether in this case the operation was correctly performed. And learn how to do it better next time so that others won't die. Or, at least, not so often.

"Gloves. Instruments. I shall examine the heart myself. Thank you."

This was a complicated case, a so-called ventricular septal defect, commonly known as a hole in the heart. This occurs when there is an opening in the partition between the lower chambers of the heart, the ventricles. The dark venous blood mingles with the arterial, the heart becomes overstrained, children gasp and turn blue at the slightest exertion. Few of these blue babies live to adolescence.

And in this case there was an additional complication, the constriction of the lung artery so that sufficient blood could never reach the lungs to become reinvigorated. Those two things often happen together, and this was an especially difficult case.

Well, Doctor, perhaps you should feel better. This little girl, Tamara, would have died anyway; she was born doomed. Her mother told me that she used to sit by the window all day long and watch other children play. She loved her dolls and had a vivid imagination. Perhaps she could have become a poetess. Or an artist, perhaps.

There are two kinds of surgery used in cases like this. One is to enlarge the opening into the pulmonary artery with a special instrument, working by touch on the pumping heart, leaving the hole in the septum, or ventricle wall, unplugged. No recovery, but several years could be added to the child's life, and children become active. The operative mortality rate is about fifteen per cent. The second method: the heart is stopped with the help of the heart-lung machine and the ventricle wall is cut wide open. The hole between the ventricles is then either stitched up or closed with the help of a porous plastic patch. The pulmonary artery entrance is enlarged and a part of the ventricle muscle is removed.

This is new and very difficult surgery. The heart remains open for almost an hour. The blood, despite the machine, seeps through and makes the surgeon's work difficult. It is easy to damage small vessels and the valves. After it is all over, heart spasms are weak, and there is a grave danger of postoperative complications. Some thirty per cent of patients die on the table or shortly thereafter.

There she lies, this percentage. Anyway, life and death are statistics. Rather like the rate of defective manufactured goods. But what to do? Still, seventy children out of a hundred survive, go to school and marry. After the second operation, marriage is permissible.

But this little one didn't make it.

I can see it all now. I have put in the stitches sloppily. Some of the sutures are placed too close to the edge of the patch. But the opening into the pulmonary artery I had enlarged well; I can push my finger into it. However, this is no consolation. With the hole between the ventricles this is even worse. Lungs fill with blood. Edema, death.

Everything is quite clear, Professor. Newspapermen can continue to sing dithyrambs to you. Young doctors can look upon you with awe and admiration. But in fact you murdered this little girl, to be frank about it. Or butchered her, as they often say about surgeons.

There is no escape. All that I can do now is drop the

lancet and at least tell all those present what I think of myself and my operation. It helps. A little.

No, that is not enough. Perhaps I'd better stop doing this sort of surgery altogether. I've had enough of these little girls with pigtails. Up to here. I've had enough of this stupid thing called life with its heartache and constant irritation. But no, this is not that easy. I must study this case and try to figure out a better way of putting in those damned sutures. It is so easy to do this now. No rush, no hysteria. The heart no longer quivers, no longer tries to pump blood which is no longer there. And the nylon bows in the pigtails which I saw yesterday protruding from under the sheet are also dead now and no longer frighten me.

So, let's see. Probably *this* is the way I should have done it. Then I would have missed the heart nerve, and the sutures would have held better. Yes, that's it. Better luck next time.

Now I must thank our dissecting-room manager, Serafima Petrovna, and leave.

"Please look out for those ribbons, don't let them get smeared with blood."

I lift the latch and find myself in the garden among the young lindens. (The latch on the door is a precaution against relatives who sometimes burst into the morgue during autopsies. One must be humane. Still, autopsies, unpleasant as they are, are extremely useful, they help to determine mistakes, and teach us how not to repeat them.)

The green lindens in the brilliant sun. The fragrance of last night's rain. What a joke!

So this difficult ordeal is over. One always tries to

push unpleasant things out of one's memory, to get over them quickly. Then they seem to be easier to bear.

I should not have been in such a hurry yesterday. The machine could have worked a little longer. I should have stopped, pinched off the aorta, removed the blood with a sucker, and checked on the patch and the sutures again. One should never be so sure.

Yes, but on the other hand it was already forty minutes since we had disconnected the heart. The machine ruins the red corpuscles, the erythrocytes. With each minute, toxic circulatory residues build up in the tissues. Then the heart is given the impossible task of clearing them out. One often sees perfect patches during autopsies. So what did they help?

And then that pale little face protruding from under the sheet. And that fear which slowly fills me during surgery, and grows with each twist of the knife. She will not come to . . . the heart will not start up . . . and her father and mother walking in the street outside the clinic, up and down, up and down. . . . I saw them when I was washing my hands. So, "Let's stitch it up! It looks pretty good."

Of course I should have stopped and made sure, checked on the patch and on every suture.

What's the use of thinking about it, now?

I walk into our experimental laboratory. In my day's program there is still a little time before my next operation. Anyway, I'm hardly in a mood for any surgery at the moment. I must cool off.

The laboratory is my love. My latest love. In my life I have had many emotional involvements, poetry, women, surgery, automobiles, my little granddaughter. Now, when my life is drawing to its inevitable conclusion, I have but one passionate desire, to learn the meaning of human life, of humanity. And what we must all do, the young and the old, in this frightening age when time has got out of hand and everything is rushing on so madly. To me the human race appears like a giant surging aloft, but with fetters on his feet. At any moment it can be pulled back, crash down, burn to cinders and disappear. It is like a nightmare wherein one knows that one must shout, must warn someone. But who? And how?

However, our laboratory has more modest aims. All that we are trying to do is lower the mortality rate among our patients. That's all. For the moment.

The Director of the Institute has given us a small building and appointed the staff. We have started working. There is a workshop, several engineers and technicians, physiologists and laboratory assistants. This is not yet an organized working collective, but their youth gives me hope.

At this point the apparatus for artificial blood circulation, our heart-lung machine, which we call AIK after the Russian words *apparat iskusstvennogo krovoobrashchenia,* interests me more than anything else. It is necessary to improve it to the point where the surgeon will have more time to operate and the machine will not ruin the blood. Our problem number one is hemolysis. As the erythrocytes are destroyed, the hemoglobin enters the plasma and colors it red. And, strange as it may seem, it then becomes toxic to the heart and the kidneys.

Petya, Misha and Oleg built our machine some two years ago, one of the very first machines of this kind ever constructed. Petya and Misha are factory lads, enthusiasts.* They started out as lathe hands, but now they are engineers. Oleg is a physician. Together they made a fine team. As long as we used our AIK for simple operations, we were very happy with it. We thought it was the best in the world because it used a mere seven hundred and fifty cubic centimeters of blood instead of the three or four liters used abroad. We bragged shamelessly about it.

But then came disappointments. Hemolysis! The heart could not remain disconnected for longer than thirty or forty minutes. For us this time is insufficient for any really advanced surgery. So I am pressing our physiologists, engineers and technicians to find the reason for hemolysis and to eradicate it, but without enlarging the amount of blood used in the machine. Everyone is breaking his head over it, but so far without success.

A new engineer has joined our laboratory, Volodya Tamasoff. Actually he is not yet fully fledged, he is still a student, but he has been accepted here as an engineer. I have high hopes for this boy. He has left the Institute of Automatics, a currently glamorous specialty, to accept a lower position in medicine. Has taken a step into the unknown, so to say. I very much like young people like that, intent, alert, independent.

I am now sitting with him in our artificial-blood-circulation laboratory.

"Volodya, I'd like to hear your report about your first reconnaissance into the hemolysis problem."

"You are in too much of a hurry, Professor. I can't tell you anything definite. Not yet."

* *Entusiasti*—volunteers who work without pay to acquire higher skills and, ultimately, well-paid positions.

"Tell me what you can. We haven't much time."

"I think that hemolysis occurs when there is an excessive turbulence in the pump and connective tubes. We must study carefully the conditions of fluid movement. Also it is quite possible that erythrocytes are crushed in the pump by the rollers. It may be necessary to leave a layer of blood between all moving parts."

"But there are American works, I have read them myself, which maintain that pressure does not produce hemolysis."

"So what? There are all kinds of works. We must check on everything ourselves, and check well. Frankly, the entire system of experimental work in our laboratory is inefficient. Measurements are not precise enough, the uniformity of conditions is not maintained, some assistants don't know how to work with precision instruments."

"Really?"

"Absolutely. If you want to do really serious work, let me bring some order into the experimental methods here, so that we can produce data we can trust and work with."

This statement surprises me. Our physiologists have been conducting experiments, our biochemists have been studying hemolysis and carrying out all sorts of analyses, and up to now there has never been any question of sloppiness or inefficiency.

I am thinking. The laboratory director, Victor Petrovich, even though young, is already a science candidate. Our girls, Alla, Nadya, Mila, Sveta, have been working with us for several years, have shared with us all the joys and despairs of creating the machine, and are servicing it now. So what shall I tell them? "To one side, kids.

This new engineer, and not even an engineer, but a student, will now teach you how to do your work, to conduct experiments and analyses."

Suddenly I hear a wail?—*"A-a-a-ah!"*

Everything turns dark all round me, everything dies. Even the trees seem to be bending.

Something snaps inside.

To hell with medicine, to hell with the hemolysis problem! I can't stand all this any longer! I must go away. Run. Hide in my office. Close all the windows. Disappear. Cease to exist. Dissolve.

"I must go, Volodya. Tell Victor Petrovich that I want him to listen to your suggestions, to study them. If he has any queries, let him speak to me."

I am walking through two laboratory rooms. Everyone avoids looking at me. Quite rightly!

Now, across the garden. From the morgue, more heartbreaking wailing. It is surprising how the sound carries. The patients who have been walking in the garden slowly drift inside. They are probably ashamed to look at me. How will they feel now, going into the operating theater with me waiting inside when their turn comes? Dreadful.

Near the entrance to the clinic sit mothers of the children who have been admitted. Of course, they also hear everything. And probably know the woman who is screaming. They all know one another, companions in misery. I am running the gantlet of their disturbed eyes. And in my soul I want to shout: "Take your children away! Can't you see that I am at the end of my rope?"

The wailing grows more desperate, more animal-like. I steal a quick glance in the direction of the morgue. A small service truck stands near it, with a little coffin on it, and wreaths. They must have ordered it last night. A woman is lying across the coffin, hugging it. *Her* mother. Damn!

Finally I reach my office. But even from here I can hear that poor woman. Now I must sit down and quietly think everything out. Quietly, if possible . . .

But no, this does not work. A quick knock at the door and a woman bursts in. Her eyes are insane.

"Professor! Please tell me what to do. I'm afraid of surgery. It's the second operation! She won't live through it!"

Again . . . What can I tell her? I'm not God. Yes, quite possibly she won't live through it. But why should *I* live through all this?

I know this woman. She is young and probably even pretty. But now she's a fright to look at. Her husband is a middle-aged man with a shy, soft face. The only child, Maya, is twelve, a tall, gawky, pleasant girl. Three months ago, my assistant, Maria Vasilievna, performed a routine operation on her, tied off the opening between the aorta and the pulmonary artery. This is a congenital heart disorder. This opening, normal in the fetus, should close after birth, but sometimes it doesn't, and then it should be closed surgically. It is the simplest of all heart operations. In our clinic we have done over a hundred of them, and lost just one patient. In Maya's case, some friends and acquaintances had called me before the operation and begged me to perform it personally rather than let some of my younger colleagues do it. Such requests always irritate me. How would young surgeons acquire their experience?

The operation had gone off well. The connection was

closed with the help of a special apparatus recently developed in Moscow using tantalum-wire stitches.

However, almost immediately there were some mildly unpleasant aftereffects, to which I paid scant attention, I had many more serious cases on hand.

At first we thought that the complications were more or less routine, the darkening of one pulmonary lobe due to the accumulation of bronchial phlegm and seeping in of air from the alveoli. The phlegm was drained through a tube inserted into the respiratory canals. The darkening remained, and a cavity appeared, a lung abscess. The pus was drained through a puncture. Maya's condition did not appear particularly alarming. The punctures were repeated, some medications were administered and in about three weeks the cavity disappeared. The darkening in the lobe had all but dissolved, and the girl was sent home.

But the very next day her mother ran to us with terror-filled eyes: Maya was spitting blood. Hemoptysis. We took several X rays, several analyses, and again discovered nothing alarming. Not that we could quite explain it, but we felt that there was little to worry about. We reassured the mother, apparently a breach in some small vessel; it often happens after pulmonary abscesses. It would pass.

But it didn't pass.

Three days ago the girl was brought back to the clinic with severe lung hemorrhage. It had happened twice during last night. The hemoglobin count had fallen off fifty per cent. I personally conducted a thorough fluoroscopic examination, a rather large darkening in the upper part of the left lung connected with a shadow of the heart and the aorta.

We think that the source of hemorrhaging is in the lung: it is possible that the abscess had not fully healed and the secondary inflammatory process then damaged the wall of some important artery. Perhaps even the aorta? Judging by the rate and severity of hemorrhaging it is quite obvious that quick death is indicated. There is just one alternative, surgical interference, and the quicker the better.

We proposed emergency surgery the day before yesterday, but the parents refused permission. Yesterday also.

And now Maya's mother is in my room. Her father, I know, sits on a bench outside, under the windows of the children's ward.

It is difficult for me to look at this woman.

"Your Mayachka needs an operation. Otherwise she will be gone, and gone very soon. You must give your permission. Dangerous? Yes, very. But otherwise, it's hopeless."

She is sobbing.

"Why, oh why has this happened to us? Why didn't you operate yourself?"

"That wouldn't have altered anything. It's routine surgery and it's been done correctly. We cannot foresee and avoid all the complications after any major surgery."

The dry official words. And my face is also dry and official. I would have liked to calm her down, to dry off her tears with a handkerchief. Or cry with her a little. But I can't permit myself this luxury. I represent science. I feel terrible.

"Professor, dear Professor, please save my daughter, save our Mayachka! We trust only you, your golden hands. I beg you."

She needn't beg me. I was planning to operate myself in any event. So I promise. She thanks me. Finally she walks to the door, dragging her feet. She stops there, turns, looks at me like a dying animal.

"Please, forgive me for saying it. But try to do it well, all right? Please."

Please! Oh my God! What must I do to survive it all, to carry with me all this human pain? The operation will be extremely dangerous, Maya may well die on the table. What would I tell her mother then? Inevitably I should be at fault; it is impossible for a surgeon not to make some slight mistake which can prove fatal to a patient in this condition. So I should shrug my shoulders, mutter some miserable words of self-justification uttered in a usual self-righteous tone. "Science is not omnipotent. It's fate. You must bear it." Bear it? How?

And the most ridiculous part of it is that I don't need it all. I don't need operations like this, either for money, or for glory, or even for my own vanity and self-gratification. I've had more than enough of all that. But what to do? Let Maria Vasilievna do it again? She is an excellent surgeon and performs routine surgery better than I. But this is not a routine case, it is very complicated and uncertain. And then if the girl dies while I'm operating it's one thing; if someone else, it's another. For the mother at least. She would always think: If only the Professor had operated himself, perhaps Maya would still have been alive.

Besides, my dear friend, you are in charge of the clinic. You must perform all the most dangerous things. Until you become convinced that your assistants know how to do it better than you.

There is no escape.

And what if we don't operate? She will die. Yes, but she would die a natural death, not from my hands. This is quite simple to arrange. All I have to do is to express the slightest uncertainty, and the parents will immediately back out. Everything would be in order, as the Germans say. "Unfortunately we were unable to secure the parents' permission."

Simple? Not to them. They would suffer. They would suffer in any event. If they refuse and she dies, "Why did we refuse?" If they agree and she dies, "Why did we allow him to do it? Perhaps she would have got well by herself!"

Of course I know that she won't get well, not one chance in a hundred. Her only hope is surgery. The risk? I think about fifty per cent. Percentages again. Just as in bookkeeping. No, there is no escape. I must order the girl to be prepared for surgery.

I call up, give all the instructions.

I have some time now. So I will visit the wards, the third floor; there are fine kids there. They are already out of danger, and they don't really need me at all. But *I* need them. Especially today, right now, before facing the terrible task ahead.

A long corridor. Not very wide, not very light, not too clean. Several tables for nurses along the walls. A large recess with windows and an enclosed balcony, here we have the children's dining room. Now children are playing here. Some have already had their operations and will soon be sent home. Others are undergoing observation. No really difficult cases here. Just normal-looking kids.

Two boys are playing with a toy automobile. It is shot to pieces, there are no wheels, no steering wheel, no top;

obviously it has passed through many small hands. In another corner three little girls are playing hospital. I stop near the nurse's vacant desk, pick up some reports, feign business. The girls are sitting on the floor, dolls in hands. The conversation:

"You need probing. This is not painful, don't cry, don't be scared. When you first feel the needle, shut your eyes and repeat 'no pain, no pain.' That's all. Masha, pass me the probe!"

Masha is five. Her medical education is limited; she does not know what a probe is. Nadya is very upset.

"How can you be a doctor this way? Even a ward nanny knows what a probe is! Where have you been all your life? All right, just hold the patient and watch. Sonya, switch on the X ray!"

It is remarkable how children use their imagination. With a few rags and wooden sticks they can create complicated plays. With years this faculty disappears. Unfortunate.

Misha approaches the girls. He is seven, and they have told me that he is impersonating me. Misha is an experienced man; he has undergone all sorts of tests, an operation with the AIK machine, and multiple post-operative complications. He is walking now, but still carries one shoulder lower than the other. His manner is rather gruff.

"Nadya, what a stupid woman, you don't do it right! The probing is always done in the dark. Get your patient under the bed. I'll do it myself, give her to me, stupid!"

"Don't touch her! This is our patient! Go and do your own operations! You've already cut up two dolls and both of them died! Manya is still crying. Her mother is poor and can't buy her another one that opens her eyes! Get out of here, you butcher!"

Nadya is firing away like a machine gun. Misha is ready to grab her hair. He already reaches for it, but stops in time. He is still in slight pain and therefore vulnerable.

"Women!" He almost spits at them.

Let them fight. It is good when children begin to roughhouse after surgery. True, some of them can take the clinic apart, and one must restrain them.

Another little boy. He is not playing. He is sitting in the corner watching others. Another blue baby. He is down for complicated, perhaps dangerous surgery. It's best not to look at him. It is better not to become too friendly with children before they are operated on. During my morning rounds I look at their chests, check their hearts. I try not to look at their faces. After surgery, well, that's another matter. Then you can love them all you want, without danger.

I walk on. At the end of the corridor there is a large room separated from the others by a glass partition. This is our postoperative ward.

Maria Dmitrievna is in charge here. She is still only a nurse, but she runs the place with an iron hand. She is perhaps forty, thin, reserved, severe, even tough. No nonsense with children, no mollycoddling, but a great deal of real love.

This is a difficult place. Some six to eight children are always recovering here from postoperative shock. The moment they are out of it, they are taken to other wards. There are no easy cases here. Two nurses and a hospital nanny run the place. In the course of the day they carry out a number of complicated tasks, injections, transfusions, enemas, stomach pumps, massaging, moving, feeding, wound dressing, et cetera, et cetera. And, after all, these are children. They cry, they play up, one must have great patience with them.

Today it is comparatively quiet here. I walk around, greet the children, talk to them. And, of course, check temperature-and-analysis charts. This is a pleasant task for me today, all the patients are doing fairly well.

Somewhere, deep in my subconscious, there is a nagging thought about Maya, about the coming operation. I am trying to drive it away. There will be time for this, for this ever-mounting fear. But meanwhile, let's look at these children.

Volodya is four. When I approach his bed, he shuts his eyes, he pretends to be asleep, but his eyelids are quivering. This is his protective reaction: he knows that doctors don't like to disturb sleeping children. He hopes to avoid injections by pretending to sleep.

"Volodineka, open your eyes. You are not asleep."

No reaction.

"Open your eyes. There won't be any injections now. Anyway, I hope to discontinue them."

The eyelids quiver, then move. He sees there is no danger. I don't even have a stethoscope. And Maria Dmitrievna is not around. He wakes up, smiles. Moves his hand to shake mine.

"It's true that you'll call off shots?"

"True, but not today. Perhaps tomorrow."

Now he's upset.

All children are pleasant. This has a purely biological foundation. When you take a child into your arms, you experience a feeling which can't be expressed in words.

For some reason no one has invented the right word for it.

And the children who have been "suffered through" are especially dear. Not only to parents, but to surgeons as well. They become precious, they carry in them a part of your soul.

This Volodya was operated on four days ago using the artificial-blood-circulation machine. He had a hole in the ventrical partition wall with some important secondary pulmonary changes.

We opened his chest and cut through the pericardium, the heart bag. Even then the heart beats became irregular. We began to hurry. The machine was not yet connected when fibrillation occurred, the disorganized fluttering instead of regular spasms. My own heart went into the pit of my stomach. Such a fine boy. I tried heart massage, he didn't respond. Then, in desperation, we inserted a tube into his right auricle and a metallic cannelure into the femoral, or thigh, artery. The machine took over. Just in time.

The operation itself was fairly easy. The hole was stitched up without a patch. The ventricle wall was closed. The machine was stopped. The heart took over strong and clear. The question which started to torture us was whether the brain had been damaged. In our panic no one could tell definitely how much time had gone between the heart massage and the time the machine was connected. If over five minutes, the cerebral cortex, the higher brain, would be destroyed, then a person becomes incapable of thought, a sort of human vegetable. For a time the boy's pupils were enlarged, a bad sign. True, they became normal after a while, but still . . . We finished the operation in dead silence.

Dmitri Alexeyevich, our chief anesthetist, and his girl assistants did everything possible to normalize the blood indices, and finally they succeeded. But the boy would not wake up. For three hours we all sat round him. The heart worked well, the breathing was normal, the lips rosy, but he would not open his eyes. We started to lose hope. I went out to smoke, to be alone with my misgivings. Suddenly Tatyana, the anesthetist's assistant, burst wildly into the room.

"He has opened his eyes!"

I ran all the way to the postanesthesia room. Yes, indeed, the eyes were open. True, they were still senseless and sleepy, but open!

"Volodya, Volodineka, my darling!"

He turned his head. Whew! I could go. There, downstairs, his mother was probably going through agony. But all was well, quite well. So far. He had opened his eyes!

Today Volodya's mother is sitting beside his bed. The operation was a success, her little son smiles, eats, sleeps; it seems that all fears are now over. She is happy. Her eyes sparkle.

Poor mothers, how often this postoperative bliss is misleading. In the depths of the little body the enemy forces might be slowly assembling, to deliver a crushing blow during one of the nights. In the course of a few hours—no, minutes—everything could be utterly destroyed. Perhaps phlegm is accumulating in one of the lungs, the nest of future pneumonia, or a blood clot is forming at the point of some inner suture, ready to break away and cause thrombosis in one of the brain arteries. There are many dangers hanging over little patients. To detect them in time, Maria Dmitrievna is constantly watching the blood pressure and taking blood for analysis, and Nina Nikolayevna, the physician, checks hearts several times each day and takes daily X rays.

"Professor, everything is all right now? There's no further danger? I'm so grateful to you!"

"The danger is still there, but it diminishes every hour. And you'd better save your thanks for the day when you will be taking Volodya home with you."

Another little boy, also Vova. He was operated on yesterday. His condition is still serious, and he lies inertly, with half-closed eyes and a rusty smear in the corner of his mouth; apparently he has been vomiting. He has constant transfusions, physiological saline solution, plasma, whole blood. There is a tube inserted into each nostril, oxygen feeding. The urine drops through a catheter. A blood-pressure band encircles his arm. He is given injections every two or three hours. His mother, a collective-farm worker, looks at him with terror in her eyes. She feels every injection in her own body and instinctively attempts to grip the nurse's arm. She is constantly weeping, paralyzed with fear and depressed by the unusual surroundings. She does more harm than good by remaining here. Maria Dmitrievna wants her taken out of the ward.

But today I can't do it. The vision of Tamara on the dissecting table, and of Maya and her mother stand before my eyes. Let this mother look at her Vova. I think that tomorrow, or the day after, she will calm down. There is nothing basically wrong with the boy, and I hope there won't be any complications. The operation was well done and was radical. All will be well with Vova.

I must now visit Lenochka. She has been moved to another ward, sharing it with two women. She has lived seven years since birth, and seven days after her operation. Perhaps this was her second birth, because death stood right behind her. I don't want to remember this struggle, all those nightmarish complications. Terror and utter despair seized me several times and I violently, inexcusably swore at my assistants, even though they were not to blame for what was happening, or at least, very little. But all this is past. Almost all. I don't think anything really dramatic can happen now if, only eight days after the operation, things go so well.

I sit near her bed. I want to caress her, to touch her, to hear her voice.

"How are you doing, Lenochka? Slept well?"

She lifts her long lashes and under them I see her sky-blue eyes.

"Quite well," she drawls, a little coquettishly. (My darling!) "They don't give me any shots any more, and I'm moving into the sixth ward. Only my daddy had to leave . . ."

She is well scrubbed and well groomed. Two thick pigtails are beautifully plaited and tied with satin ribbons. (Who is braiding the hair of *that* girl before she is put into her little coffin? Her mother probably can't do it. All right. Enough!)

Our laboratory girls are probably responsible for Lenochka's elegance. We have a flock of young girls working downstairs who like to come up here and take care of their favorites. I don't think her father could have done it quite so well, and the nurses are too busy to give beauty treatments to the patients, they have their hands full watching over their health.

Lena's father is some sort of mechanic. Her mother has a small child at home and could come here for two days only. They live some fifty kilometers away. So the father had to take over. However, our nurses like fathers. They say that men are more sensible and don't panic so easily. And this particular father has repaired all sorts of equipment around the ward during the last seven days. He is very handy with tools.

Parents are a difficult problem. We don't allow anyone into postoperative wards for adults—"to prevent infection," as we explain. But here, parents stay with their children though the danger of infection is even more serious. This is our concession to pity. It is difficult—no, impossible—to drive parents away when their children are hovering between life and death. Your tongue just wouldn't move to order them out. Some of them actually help the nurses and nannies with simple tasks; we are somewhat understaffed, and extra hands can always be used. But most of them get in the way. It takes special training to be useful in a hospital ward. One must have strong nerves, or at least be accustomed to the sight of suffering. There are a few nasty parents too; they become hysterical or are just mean. They think that all doctors are heartless and all nurses lazy and cruel. They think that we actually want to murder their children. Parents like these must be kept out, despite their loud threats to complain. The actual complaints, however, are extremely rare. Perhaps later, after considering quietly and soberly, they realize the shamefulness of their behavior. It is impossible not to see the sacrificial hard work going on within these walls day and night.

There are also impudent types. They filter into the

wards through the back entrance, and some even bring their own hospital robes. We suspect that one old woman in the admission ward is helping them, taking presents for it.

"Professor, you are wanted in the theater!"

"In a minute. Just as soon as I complete the rounds."

Listen, my dear fellow, enough of wasting time on small nonsense. Enough of procrastination. Go and do your most important work. Lenochka and Volodya don't need you here, they are well on the way to recovery. Vova will live also. So there is some justification for your work, before God or before yourself. And that's the main thing.

2

MAYA

I GO TO THE THEATER. Further delay is impossible. Everything inside me is taut. All feelings have contracted into a little clot and are hidden in the far corner of my subconscious. The whole world is clear. Black and white.

I am dressing. The glasses. The surgical mask. There are small disorders near the entrance, but I must remain calm. I can't afford to fritter my nerves away. There will be more ample reasons for that.

Maya is already in the operating theater. The tube has been inserted into the trachea, the anesthesis apparatus has been connected. She is asleep. My assistants, Maria Vasilievna, Pyotr Alexandrovich and Volodya are dressing the operating field with sterilized sheets.

Now that I'm here they will start. The theater nurse, Marina, a serious, lithe, beautiful woman, is standing near the instrument table. She is quite ready, and so are the others. We have a fine team here.

I wash my hands in the theater antechamber. Without words, and almost without thoughts. In the subconscious everything has been thought out, yesterday, today, a few minutes ago in the children's wards. I scrub my hands with one brush. Another. A sterilized towel. I am ready.

I enter the theater. They hand me a napkin and some alcohol. I put on my robe.

"Fix the light. Why can't you ever put it on properly for an operation?"

Stop! I must not get wound up. Anyway, they won't do it properly next time no matter what I say. Let them be.

Maya is lying on her right side. The scar has been cut away and the clamps are being put on small blood vessels. Maria Vasilievna's movements are precise and economical; she seems to be the embodiment of quiet efficiency. But this is misleading. She is a highly nervous woman, and when she operates on her own she often grumbles. A good surgeon with steel-like nerves is fiction, just like an actor who does not get nervous before his entrance. One must get nervous, otherwise he is in the wrong profession. I make all these notes with a small part of my brain. Marina is handing instruments over to Maria Vasilievna in response to her finger snaps, without words, knowing what is needed. She is very experienced and has been working with me for years. An excellent nurse. No, a trusted assistant.

The gloves. Alcohol again. I take my place, take over. I cut through intercostal muscles and get into the pleural cavity. It is filled with commissures. The lung has become connected to the chest cavity wall, a normal picture after surgery. The commissures are hard, I can't separate them with my fingers; I must use the lancet or scissors. There is a good deal of bleeding; it must be coagulized or simply checked by electric diathermy. Puffs of smoke and the smell of burnt flesh.

Everything is done practically without thinking, by reflex. I can see the operating field, the lung. In my head there is a definite plan, with variations; it is carried out step by step with simple mechanical movements. The hand movements replace thought. A move, one look, an instant evaluation of the situation, a new move. The whole world is temporarily disconnected from me; one can work like this for six hours without feeling fatigue. Of course, only when the operation is challenging. Otherwise it is like any other repair work; one becomes almost a mechanic. But this case is challenging and difficult, or rather, will be difficult.

Just as soon as the upper lobe of the lung is separated from the pectoral wall, it becomes obvious that a tissue density, resembling a tumor, is located along the vessels leading away from the heart, on the aortal arch, on the pulmonary artery. The lung is just attached to it and even though the tissue has thickened, the source of the hemorrhaging must be there, in the large vessels. When I press on the tumor with my finger I can feel it pulsate.

Aneurysm! Aneurysm of the aorta!

The clinical picture becomes instantly clear. After the first operation an abscess occurred in the lung, and the inflammation has ruined the aortal wall. A cavity has formed attached to the aorta—the aneurysm—a widening of the artery caused by the changes in its wall. It has broken through into a bronchial tube with resulting hemorrhaging. Any further hemorrhage may prove to be fatal.

Everything is very clear, and very bad, much worse than I had expected. There is an abscess in the lung, and an opening in the aorta. The area of the aneurysm covers a part of the aortal arch. All this is covered with commissures, hard as gristle. Besides all this, inflammation of the lung tissue.

My hands continue to work automatically, separating commissures and coming closer to the aneurysm. There is just one thought in my mind, what to do next? While working, one feels calmer, and it seems to me that I don't quite appreciate the gravity of the situation.

I must stop, wash my hands. This is a pause for thought and a cool appraisal of the situation.

So, there are two alternatives.

First, to stitch up the wound and abandon the operation. Retreat is still possible. The case may be written down as inoperable.

The picture: outside the mother runs to me. "All is well? Maya will live?" Alas, no, she will die and die very soon. There was nothing we could do. Or, rather, it was too dangerous, she could easily have died on the table. And this way? Silence. Were there any chances at all? Yes, but not many. I had no right to take them. Then why did you try? I did not know the exact situation before the operation. What shall we do now, take her to Moscow? No, impossible. She would die in the plane.

A pause. A look.

The picture continues. The girl is brought into the ward. Pale little face. Eyes full of hope. Then, a little later, a coughing spell. Blood. A lot of blood. Another look, full of bewilderment. What has happened? What about the operation? Of course, a professor is not obliged to be in the ward. The interns can do everything, especially because there is not much that can be done, except futile blood transfusions. So I knew what would happen? Yes. And was afraid to be blamed for butchering the girl? No. What was I afraid of then? The morgue, the funeral, the mother's tears? Yes. Then you shouldn't be a doctor.

Another alternative, to try to separate the aorta above and below the aneurysm, as close to it as possible. And the pulmonary artery. And the lobe of the lung. Then pinch off the aorta and quickly cut away the aneurysm along with part of the lung. Then stitch up the aortal wall. All right, but one can pinch off the aorta for a maximum of ten minutes, and only if the vessels leading to the brain are above the clamp. Any longer period would destroy the spinal cord. To do all that in ten minutes? Impossible. But then it is possible to plug the opening with the finger, remove the clamps, let the brain be washed out by the arterial blood, and then apply the clamp again. This can be repeated several times. We have had some experience of this and it has been successful. But in Maya's case we also have commissures and the inflammation. And then it is by no means certain that the hole in the aorta can be stitched up at all, and if not—well, that's the end.

Her mother again. No words this time. Just terror in her eyes. "Dead?" Yes. I couldn't do a thing. Aneurysm. Commissures. Degeneration of inflamed tissues. They were much too brittle. Hemorrhage . . . "She's dead—dead! *A-a-a-ah!"*

But just suppose I succeed? Then in a few days I can go to the ward as I did today. "Well, Maya, my darling, how are you? Slept well?"

There is no third choice. To tie off the bronchial tube and let it go at that? The inflammation of the lung would progress and kill her just the same.

Only two alternatives. Just two choices.

It is hard to choose. Let's work a bit longer, the final decision can still be postponed a little. If the separation of the aorta and the preservation of the brain arteries prove to be impossible, the question would settle itself.

I go back to work.

The plan proves feasible. Not only possible, but almost successful. I widen part of the pericardium, separate the rising aorta, and moving down along it, reach the important vessels. I make a canal under it and run a thread through. This has been the hardest part of all. I free the aorta below the aneurysm. I do the same with the pulmonary artery. This has been a time-consuming work, the operation has already lasted for three hours, but I don't notice it. The anesthetist is silent; it means that everything is going well. I can see this myself, the pumping heart is right before my eyes. I must save every bit of my nervous energy for the future even though there are many things which irritate me. Pyotr Alexandrovich is assisting carelessly, he hasn't had enough experience of working with me. But the other two are tense, alert, efficient.

A constant blood transfusion. Every drop of blood lost on the swabs and napkins is immediately replaced.

I speak to the anesthetist. "Dmitry Alexandrovich, ask them to send us some more blood from the station. If I decide to go ahead, we shall need a great deal."

I continue. Everything goes very slowly, the separation of blood vessels from the commissures requires infinite skill. The progress is measured by split millimeters. My hands work by themselves. Thoughts are infrequent and fitful. What if we use the heart-lung machine? Then we can pinch off the aorta more easily, and there would be no pressure of time.

Unfortunately, setting up the machine takes two hours. Besides, we have no whole blood on hand. I must continue the way I have begun.

The operation goes on surprisingly well, my every move is precise and measured. I am beginning to think that I am God. That there is nothing I can't do. Just look at those separated vessels, and the lung! So clean, so dry. It is not an easy task, in view of all those commissures, to work so close to an aneurysm, it's no joke at all. Few surgeons would even risk it.

Really, after all, I'm not a bad surgeon. Perhaps one of the very best.

Stop bragging, Professor! Look at your trembling hands, they have been trembling all your life. And then remember the scene near the morgue this morning, the coffin, the wailing. Big hero, indeed!

All the preliminary operations have been completed. Even more than that, I have tied off the bronchial tube. It is still possible to retreat, but now is the time to make the final decision.

But making any decision proves to be unnecessary. Suddenly there is a geyser of blood which hits me straight in the face. Instantly the hole is found by touch and plugged by my finger.

"Clean my glasses!"

For a second I'm blind. But no matter. My finger knows what to do.

"Keep mopping up the blood in the wound!"

The aneurysm wall has burst. In one place I have cut too deep through a commissure and . . . well, I should have expected that. But it has all happened so suddenly, so dramatically.

Why didn't I stop in time?

Now, it's too late. No retreat any more. However, things are still under control. The heart works well. Quite well.

No. Not any more. Not really. Should I remove my finger, the pleural cavity would flood with blood, the blood pressure would go down to zero, and the heart would start quivering barely perceptibly, instead of beating. I must press the hole down. Like that boy in Holland who held his finger in the hole in the dike. But there they came to relieve him. No one here is going to relieve me.

"Start transfusion direct into the artery! As quickly as you can! Hurry!"

I draw in air like a diver before taking a plunge. As though this is my last breath.

"Petya, clamp off the aorta! Maria, pinch off the pulmonary artery!"

Now I remove my finger. A weak spurt of blood, then it slackens off. No pressure.

"The vacuum sucker! Goddam it, it doesn't work! Give me another one, quickly!"

I have ten minutes at my disposal. So very little. I tear open the wall of the burst aneurysm, clean out the blood clots. I must cut away a section of the lung to reach the aorta. But this is difficult to do, there are many still unseparated commissures. Whoever has built the human body has done it seemingly with just one idea in mind—to impede surgeons.

"The power shears! Quick, you cow!"

A split-second thought: Why swear? Oh, what's the difference! The section of the lung is cut away, almost torn off.

Horror.

In the aorta wall there is a hole about a centimeter long. The edges are uneven, the tissues are weakened by inflammation, they would never hold the thread. Impossible.

"What have I done, what have I done? Idiot!"

This, about myself. I am a complete nonentity, a miserable quack. Let everyone know it. I don't care. All I want is to drop dead, this very second, while that other heart is still beating. But I have no right to drop dead.

I must do something. Must try. What if the sutures will hold after all? God—grant me a miracle!

"Marina, the sutures. Check them for strength, each one."

I sew desperately, trying to put the stitches as far away from the edges as I can. But it is hopeless—the tissues are coming apart like butter, nothing holds at all. Just as I thought.

"Give me more! More! Marina!"

These hopeless, bumbling attempts take about five precious minutes. From some small vessels the blood continues to seep into the aneurysm, flooding the field. We have to tighten the pulmonary-artery clamp—or else.

"Professor, the pressure is falling off."

"Keep pouring the blood in! Open the femoral artery on the other thigh, you slobs!"

"There is no pulse."

My God, my God, what now? I can see and feel how the heart spasms grow weaker and weaker. We must remove the clamps form the aorta.

"Petya, Maria, Volodya! I'll close the hole with my finger, and you remove the clamps. All at the same time. One, two, three—now!"

The clamps are loosened. The pressure in the aorta is

low, but blood keeps seeping in from somewhere. The heart all but stops.

"Keep pouring blood in! Clean the wound with a sucker! Get adrenalin ready, three cubes!"

No, we must pinch off the aorta again, the blood floods the entire field. And I must massage the heart. It is hopeless, of course, quite useless, but it is still trying to beat. And just supposing there's a miracle? No, stupid, there are no miracles. No God.

"Petya, clamp the aorta. Maria, cut the pericardium wider for a massage. *What?* You pulled out the clamp altogether, you idiot? Where were your eyes, you bastard? We shall never get it under again—never! How can I work with such cretins?"

Various insulting epithets. I shout because I'm in despair. Petya has made a mistake of course; he should not have pulled out the clamp. But does that change anything? I remove my finger from the hole, there are sluggish little spurts; exactly like those from a barrel when the liquid is at the very bottom.

I am almost crying. I don't want to live in this horrible world where little girls die like this.

I am massaging the heart. With each squeeze a bit of blood oozes out of the aorta. I still can't attach the clamp. I am hysterical. I am swearing at Petya, and at Maria blaming her for the first operation, even though there are no reasons to suspect that anything had been done incorrectly. I am going to pieces.

Adrenalin. Massage. New transfusions. All this is painfully slow. The heart gives infrequent lazy spasms as though slowly going to sleep. But I must do something, I must, I must!

"Professor, the pupils have already been enlarged ten minutes."

The meaning of these terrible words slowly sinks in. So, this is it. Death. One must accept the fact, even though the heart continues to quiver convulsively now and then, quite unnecessarily. It is clinically dead.

"Very well, that's all. Stop the transfusion. Save the blood for those who will need it."

All of a sudden, an utter apathy comes over me. Almost a relief. But not quite. It is impossible to describe this.

"Stitch up the wound."

I stagger out into the antechamber. Toward an armchair. No, I must change first. I'm covered with blood like a butcher.

However, I sit down. My head is empty. My hands are numb. My feet throb with pain. Nothing matters any longer. Everything is over.

But no, not quite. There are Maya's mother and father. (Strange, when one thinks of a dead child's parents, mother always comes first.) Of course, they must have sensed already that things are not going well. It's been five hours since we took Maya up to surgery. But they still hope, parents never cease hoping. There is not much hope left by this time, just a little hope hanging on a slender thread of utter impossibility to accept the death of one's only child, but still it's hope, and now someone must go and sever this thread. There is no use in waiting, in putting this off. All is over. The wound is covered, the blood washed away. Maya lies covered with a sheet. No, not Maya. A corpse. I can't utter this word aloud.

Several tired doctors assemble in the room. Someone

must go and speak to the mother. Actually, I should do it, but I procrastinate, keep silent, hoping that someone will come to my rescue. Finally, Pyotr Alexandrovich turns to Volodya.

"Go and tell her mother."

Volodya can't disobey an order, we have a certain discipline, and he's a junior among us. He hates to do this, but he rises slowly and walks to the door.

Too late. We have procrastinated too long. The door bursts open and Maya's mother runs in. She looks insane, at this moment she probably is. She runs straight to the operating table and throws herself onto her daughter's corpse, just as they do in bad novels. She is sobbing some tender words. Kisses the dead blue lips.

"Wake up, Mayachka, wake up, my dearest, my darling, wake up, wake up!"

She does not utter the words I am waiting for: "What have they done to you!" She does not blame anyone—not yet. She doesn't yet realize, does not want to understand that her daughter, her precious Mayachka, is no longer here, that she is speaking to an already slowly decomposing corpse.

The room is almost empty now. It is difficult to watch this scene. Nurses are crying.

I get up, approach the woman, try to speak to her. I say some stupid dead words which I am ashamed to repeat, words I have said so many times before and have been ashamed of, every time I spoke them. Finally, with some effort, they lead her away into the postoperative room, a little room where patients spend some time after an operation before being taken into the wards. There she is sick. I don't see it because I remain in the antechamber and again sit down. Someone tells me that she is lying on the floor. On the floor? Why? Oh yes, there are no beds and no couches there, just some round white metal stools.

Then she and her husband are taken home in a hospital car. What they will do there, I don't know.

Maria Vasilievna is weeping in the corner.

Now I must write a report, a detailed one. "All attempts to close the defect in the aortal wall proved to be unsuccessful. The hemorrhage continued, and life was slowly ebbing away. . . ."

Ebbing. The day is ebbing, too. I've done my work, I can go home. The darkness is gathering outside. This is a relief. At least no one will see me. Shall I ever forget this day?

I am walking through the park under some large trees. The evening sky is clear and pale. It is very quiet here. The faint hum of the city comes from the far distance, first lights begin to appear here and there. Everything is calm and pretty. Poets write poems about this. What poems? All this is a fraud! Behind those twinkling windows people are suffering. They drink, they fight, they count money. They hate, they long for something which they will never get, they become sick. They grow old. With every second they draw closer to death. And farther, beyond the horizon, they die of hunger. Or make atom bombs, getting ready to send upon humanity an avalanche of death and pain.

The pale sky and the smell of flowers do not affect me now. I am depressed. I must think, must search. Must find some way of living with that pale sky. Only an insensitive man can just admire it, without thinking.

The door of my home. I hear a tender, ringing little voice like a silver bell.

"Who is there?"

This is my granddaughter. Lenochka. She is four. She calls me Daddy because her real father left when she was a mere baby. I love her very much. Yes, very, very much.

"Why are you so late? You had an operation?"

I lift her in my arms, kiss her. And before my eyes there stands that other little girl, the same pigtails, the same nylon ribbons. Only that other one was so thin.

"Is everything all right, Daddy? Did the patient die?"

She asks this lightly. The word dead still means nothing to her. It doesn't mean anything to anybody, not to the living; we all know that there is death, but we don't believe it. But in time we learn to pretend. Lenochka has had no time to learn this yet.

"Yes, my darling. She died."

My wife comes into the room. She is also a doctor, a good one, and during the many years of our marriage we have learned to read each other's faces. We never ask questions.

Everything is as usual. I change, put on my slippers. A silent dinner, if this can be called a dinner. Let us not dramatize things, let's pretend that nothing has happened. But I need a drink. This is essential after a day like this. I am resorting to this medicine quite often now. And why not? What do I have to lose, what to preserve?

At this point the program calls for sleep. Using this as a pretext, I can escape into my study and stretch out on my sofa. I sleep here now. My wife is a light sleeper and once awakened, she can't go back to sleep, and she needs her rest. Here I can put a bottle of cognac and a little glass on a chair next to my bed. Just like the stories of Remarque or Hemingway. Funny. Even at moments like this one succumbs to theatrical effects and compares oneself to fictional heroes. Or is this something special to me?

Tonight there won't be any sleep, not for a long while. Through my slightly befuddled brain pass the images of the day. The wailing of the woman over the coffin. The first woman. Then the second one. "Please, try to do it well, all right?" I tried, but I didn't do it well. I failed.

The door is closed and there is no one in the next room. So I can grab my head and moan: Oh, my God, my God.

Murders. Every day in hospitals throughout the world people are dying. Often because of doctors' mistakes. Especially surgeons'. It is easier for therapeutists—the patient did not respond to the medicine and he died. By himself. He couldn't be saved. Too bad, science is still very limited. Of course, Doctor, we understand, this wasn't your fault. But what when your lancet slips and an aneurysm bursts into your face?

There are different murders. A bandit kills for money or just for blood lust. This is disgusting, and they punish him with death.

A jealous man kills because he cannot endure his anguish. He gets a lighter punishment; in some cases they even let him go. Love is still respected. However, for a murderer to remain alive is often the worst punishment. Still, most of them get over it in time.

An automobile driver kills accidentally. He himself is a victim. The murder jumps at him like a wild beast and ruins his life. But what can one do? One cannot permit drivers to run people down. Let them watch out more carefully.

There is also war. Many murders, for an ideal. Or someone's profit. Or because of the mad designs of some rabid politicians. The war murder is noble. They give medals and titles for it, the more the better. People, soldiers, get used to killing quite easily. Especially now, when it is done by long distance, without smearing one's hands with blood. This is an abstract murder. Besides, for a soldier it is honest. They might as well kill him. He has no choice. He must kill, or be killed.

Then, at the bottom of the list, are surgeons. No one calls us murderers, except hysterical relatives. We have noble aims. A man is in danger, the surgeon fights for his life, and now and then he loses the battle. But what of it? One can't always win.

This is not the first time that I lie like this on this very sofa. There have been many deaths in my career. Murders? Yes, also murders. Unpremeditated murders, to use the legal jargon, but murders just the same. One must call things by their proper names. I have thought a great deal about my life, and I am thinking now. Hundreds of the most complicated operations, and a fair percentage of failures. Some deaths have been caused directly by me. But no, those were not murders! Everything within me protests against this word. I had taken calculated risks to save lives.

How sad and unpleasant I feel today. What was my mistake with Maya? I should have stopped in time. Just as soon as I saw the aneurysm, I should have stopped. Sewn up the wound. She would have lasted until tomorrow with transfusions. Tomorrow we could have set up our AIK machine, got some fresh blood. Then I could have disconnected the heart and carefully patched up the hole in the aorta, cutting away a part of the lung, without pressure, without hysteria.

Nonsense. It's not that easy at all to operate on an aneurysm, even with the heart-lung machine. It is almost hopeless, taking into consideration the patient's condition. And then she would have to be kept alive until tomorrow, a very questionable proposition.

Still, my chances would have been much better. Mistakes . . . I'm making mistakes like a small boy.

There are different operations. You operate on a mortally wounded soldier. Death is inevitable in any event. There are other hopeless cases where the surgeon's work is almost symbolic, he is supposed to do something, he tries, he makes mistakes, but that does not really matter. But Tamara and Maya? Did they have to die?

Tamara's case was especially painful. It was not even an emergency one. The girl walked into the clinic on her own feet, and she would have lived for three to four years at least, even without surgery. Then something went wrong during the operation, I still don't know exactly what, and now she is laid out on a mortuary table.

Let's have a drink.

Surgery is supposed to be a corrective science, then why do patients die so often?

There are cases when everything is done correctly, and the patient is dead. Perhaps there was a faulty calculation, the doctor was not clever enough in appraising the case. But in some cases proper calculation is impossible. The science itself is at fault.

Then, often the operation is not performed skillfully enough, somewhere the surgeon has erred, or he has not used the proper technique in this particular case. A good craftsman would have done it, but the less skilled one fails. Death! One can perform ten operations brilliantly and slip on the eleventh, and there's another fatality. A surgeon is not only a physician, he is a craftsman, like a jeweler or a toolmaker. There are good craftsmen and bad. And if you are not first-rate, you had better quit.

A surgeon must be intelligent, he must know his craft and he must keep on learning it his whole life through.

But even that is not enough. My friend, a mathematician, does not recognize medicine as a science. No exact computation, no science. He says that everything in life must be done with computers, that the human brain is much too limited. Perhaps. I don't know. I haven't absorbed this yet. But one thing is certain: as a precision machine, the human brain is imperfect; it forgets things, it mixes them up, it misplaces facts and figures fed into it. It can be put out of focus with a few small glasses of cognac. This cannot happen to a machine.

To be a good surgeon, one must not only be good with instruments, but have extensive experience to cope with unusual conditions which he may encounter. He must perform a great deal of actual surgery. And he must have a special phychological make-up for it. You see how beautifully it all sorts out into neat compartments, with a few glasses of cognac.

It means that deaths are unavoidable no matter how skillful the surgeon is. One can't wait until medicine becomes exact and faultless. This would take scores of years, perhaps centuries, and millions of patients would die waiting. One can't avoid mistakes in any work. In our work mistakes are paid for with lives. To become a craftsman one must practice, must ruin the material he is working with. Our material is people.

This is terrible, but you can't change it.

Therefore, there is no point in going to pieces because two little girls died who would have died anyway. No one can possibly blame you for it. The important thing is honest intention. And no pecuniary considerations, no money—an honest man can't do this kind of work for money. Then you can come home from your work, have a drink and go to bed. And if your nerves are weak, well, you're in the wrong profession, that's all.

Lenochka comes into the room to bid me goodnight. After her bath, she is so clean, so pink. She is glowing with health and joy of living.

"Goodnight, Daddy. You're drinking cognac? Walk with me to bed."

"Goodnight, my darling. No. Go alone tonight. I'm very tired. I must rest."

She kisses me and runs away stumbling in her long nightie, chirping like a bird.

Most likely I'm not fit to be a surgeon. I'm too sentimental, too soft. I shouldn't be in work which kills people.

They say there is a proper percentage of fatalities after different kinds of surgery. The world's statistics of mistakes and failures. In our country? The level is about normal, a little more here, a little less there. Figures don't lie. But one doesn't see the dead behind the figures. Their photographs are not printed in medical journals.

That first girl, Tamara, had such serious eyes.

And Maya was so gay, so full of life.

The past tense. Had. Was.

Let's have another little glass.

Cognac tastes particularly bitter tonight. No, I won't become an alcoholic.

Feeling sorry for yourself again? Don't. After all, not everyone dies. Those children you saw in the convalescent ward today, they were wonderful. And all those former patients who come for a checkup every Monday. Grown-up, smiling, handsome. You look at them and all the bitterness inside melts away. And you go back to surgery and do more work.

I have been in surgery for thirty years. That's a long time. I started out as a young dreamer, transplantation of organs, rejuvenation. The lancet the crowning glory of medicine. Home practitioners, a lower form of life. "I will accomplish miracles!" When I think about myself as I was then, I feel a little contempt and a tinge of sadness. Regrets? No. Generally speaking, I have lived a good life. Nothing spectacular, but good and honest. Aspirant, assistant, reader, professor. Almost like those doctors portrayed in plays and novels, limited, slightly comical pedants?

No. Surgery has given me such passions, as nothing else could have done. I am a creator, I am a doer. My conscience is my only judge. And what else can impose upon one a more severe judgment?

Words, beautiful words. It has been such hard labor, all the way.

Tonight I am lying on my sofa, crushed, a little drunk, all my dreams of accomplishment just as remote as they were thirty years ago.

No, that's not true. It's sorrow and disappointment

which speak in me tonight. And fatigue. Much has been accomplished.

Back in the 'thirties simple stomach operations and kidney removals were regarded as almost miraculous achievements. Only our master surgeons very rarely and timidly attempted to touch the pectoral cavity, with almost uniformly unsuccessful results. Then, for a while, they discontinued it altogether. And now my assistants perform routine heart surgery every day, and the patients recover.

All this has cost us many lives and a great deal of suffering, but today we can show profits for our labors.

How little we knew at that time, how unsure we were of our methods! But gradually there was progress. Blood transfusion, local anesthesia, various accomplishments in prophylaxis and diagnosis. Fewer and fewer deaths. You grow bold, you start on the more difficult cases with supreme confidence, and—bang, bang!—you fall flat on your face. "Why did I try this? Why didn't I stop in time?" But then you cool off, evaluate your mistakes and start out again, like all other surgeons throughout the world.

After the war we really started on the chest, lungs, esophagus. I was already a professor then. That, however, is not an important point. Surgery makes everyone equal, a young doctor and an academician—just show us your skill, what you can do. And as to the degrees and titles, they are merely for the pay rate. That is what rank-and-file doctors think; in reality, professors and academicians consider themselves superior beings. They are the initiated. Many of them have forgotten their fears and misgivings when they were defending their miserable dissertations, and naïvely believe that they have made a lasting contribution to science.

Many? And how about yourself and your "Variations of Diaphragmal Nerve Behavior"?

But let's not be supercritical. I have worked hard and honestly. I have never put too much stress on my degrees and titles. They are good to have, one can get a better clinic, better conditions for experimental surgery.

1949. The first pneumonectomy. Six and a half hours. The patient in deep shock, and I collapse on a divan. True, it was a difficult case. He got over it. That was very exciting. Where is he now, my Semyon, my Senya, as I used to call him fondly? I haven't seen him for five years. The last time I saw him he was a rural postman. "I walk at least twenty kilometers every day." A pleasant memory! And he was once doomed.

There have been many such Semyons in my career; how could I have survived otherwise? But somehow these happy memories don't come to me tonight. After Semyon there was Pavlik, with a chronic lung abscess. The hemorrhage and artery damage. He died. I was lying on this very sofa then, just like tonight.

But nonetheless we have conquered the lung, today we can operate almost with a guarantee. I have also made some contribution here. No, let's forget that. I thought I had developed a new technique of bronchial-tube surgery only to learn that it had been discovered before. So much for my contribution.

No, let's be honest. I have assembled some fine experience material and developed a good method. Have been teaching it to surgeons. Many of them are now using my findings, and using them well. Patients recover, thank their doctors. This is a definite credit to a craftsman working with the most precious material of all—people.

How difficult self-criticism is! Had I not had tragic days like today, I probably would have thought myself a rare talent, like some of my colleagues. This is also not true. I'm no more conscientious than others.

Then we started heart surgery. Again the whole procession of faces and dates. My first patient, a woman with an advanced stenosis and heavy decompensation. An intelligent woman, she well knew that she was doomed. A widow. "I want to live just a few years longer, I must raise my son." Why didn't she go to Moscow? They were performing those operations there. I don't know. But I will be forever grateful to her for the trust she put in me. She was very lucky not to die on the table, I grow red in the face when I think of that operation. I was so awkward, so frightened. But she is alive today. And her son has grown up. I'm so thankful to her.

Yet the heart is the most difficult area. It will probably prove to be my undoing. Why do I do it then? For the love of my fellowmen? Keep quiet, doctor. You're doing it for yourself.

There has been joy, but also many disappointments. The results were often unsatisfactory. We must learn to open the heart and replace all its component parts.

Then the epic story of the construction of the AIK. Yes, it was a high adventure, a true epic, with all the human passions. Had I been a writer I could have written a book about it. Honestly, I was partly instrumental here. Of course, without Oleg, Pyotr, Maria, Dima and many others, the whole thing would not have been possible. It was a real collective effort.

Do they like me?

They used to, but now I don't know. I'm becoming more and more detached from them. I'm drying up inside, I'm becoming irritable, intolerant, dour. They probably ascribe this to my sense of self-importance.

I remember our first operation with the AIK. It was a failure. For a whole year afterward we worked with dogs, improving the machine. Then, the first success! A little boy Kolya, another blue baby with a hole in the heart, the ventricular septal defect. The operation was not really radical, but he survived and improved. That was a great achievement. In the entire Soviet Union there were only a few clinics then with records of successful cases. I remember our pride, all the emotional turmoil. Our confidence as we tackled other cases. After each operation several doctors were in constant attendance on every case, day and night.

Only the first operations were good. Then, a whole series of failures. We began to take on more and more difficult cases. But what else could we do? Who needs help more than those previously inoperable cases?

However, that was a dismal stretch.

The entire history of the so-called Big Surgery stands before my eyes. I have taken part in it, often in the front ranks. I can't say that I have achieved anything really brilliant. I'm no inventor, just a good practitioner. In time my name will be forgotten.

I don't care about that, now. But later?

Is it cognac or my depression which makes my thoughts so formless? It is some mixture of sentimentality and bitterness.

Let's have another drink, just to clear the head.

Enough! My whole life I have striven for clarity of

thought. Now I must bring some logic into my own mind.

Does humanity need surgery? Undoubtedly, yes. Not all patients die. The majority survive and enjoy life. For as long as science permits them. True, there have been many unnecessary deaths, but that is unavoidable. Unfortunate. From the dawn of time people sacrificed to various gods hoping to earn their favor.

How did the ancient priests feel, butchering children upon their altars?

Are we such priests?

One should not overglamorize surgeons. They risk other people's lives, not their own. In this respect they are not soldiers, but generals. Yet, we don't remain unscathed. We are performing hard and difficult work for the benefit of humanity. Why do we do it? Not for money. A surgeon lives no better than a family doctor, or an engineer. Vanity? Of course, while you are young it flatters your ego to be regarded as a sort of superman. But for me this no longer exists. No? Yes, it is still pleasant, but not pleasant enough to risk spectacular even though hopeless operations for the sake of this pleasure. What else then? Well, perhaps the sense of challenge, of contest, of struggle which makes the final victory so rewarding. And, finally, the duty. Perhaps you are being coy? The explanation is much too primitive. Psychologists must study the stimuli which govern all human behavior. *Stimulus* is a Latin word; it describes a prod with which the Romans used to drive on their animals. Isn't it the same thing with us?

The nature of man. What is man? This question has been posed many, many times, and the answers are just as numerous, and often completely contradictory.

Man is kind by nature.

Man is the cruelest animal in existence.

Has he a multiple image? What are good and evil? Progress? Future?

It would be good to learn the answer before death. Is it so impossible to keep all those little boys and girls happy, just as happy as they are when they have love, good health and all the material necessities of a good life? And what is happiness?

Once again I have strayed from my original line of thought.

I'm not feeling well. I'm particularly depressed tonight. This has happened to me before, but not like tonight. I've reached some sort of saturation point. Victories no longer bring the joys which they used to bring. The suffering of the unfortunate has poisoned my soul, has deprived it of peace. Old banal phrases. Clichés. Disgusting.

I am very familiar with physical suffering. But there are many other forms of suffering of which I know nothing. Humiliation, poverty, injustice, inability to communicate with others.

Then what do I want to do?

Die?

How many times this thought has come to me at moments like this. In the struggle which surgeons wage, only patients die. But when the heart stops in your hands, when you feel the quivering life ebb away—how many times have I felt like dying myself to prevent this disaster. But there is no exchange; the patient dies, and I live on. Then time passes, and I am no longer ready for this exchange. I have changed my mind. But each such bitter moment gradually ruins one's life.

The history of medicine knows the cases of surgeons' suicides. Kolomnin, the pupil of Pirogoff, inserted a massive dose of cocaine into a patient's colon. It was a well-calculated, well-thought-out action, but the patient died. Kolomnin went to his study and shot himself.

Dr. Block, a German, attempted a double lung operation at the turn of the century in the case of advanced tuberculosis. The patient died on the table. The doctor poisoned himself the same day. It was a double funeral.

Of course, reasonable people would consider these cases as temporary insanity. If this practice were accepted, all surgeons should have been dead long ago. There would be no one left to perform a simple appendectomy.

These are extreme cases and can't be considered seriously. But I, for one, take off my hat before their sense of humanity.

Perhaps you are just moralizing? You are afraid of responsibility and looking for an escape? Using humanity as a shield? I don't know. Tonight life has little meaning to me. Of course, I love my granddaughter very much. I have never loved my daughter this way. I was young then, perhaps, had other interests. But, in fact, Lenochka can grow up without me. Eugenie and Lisa would certainly know how to bring her up.

It seems to me now that I'm saying something very stupid.

No, I will not poison myself. Even though nowadays there exist such wonderful poisons. You go to sleep with beautiful dreams and never awaken. Marvelous. No more operations and mothers' tears.

All right, enough of sentiment. Such a noble hero indeed! "He could not bear it, he felt it was the best solution for everyone." They used to write this in old novels which, frankly, I can no longer read.

I'm quite drunk. Another little glass? No. Enough for tonight.

There is still another escape. I can go into pure science. Laboratory work is so pleasant. You sit, think, experiment. You feel sorry for dogs, of course, but still they are not people. Physiology is a fascinating subject. There are so many things to discover, to learn—how to control blood pressure, the effects of oxygen hunger upon tissues, shock . . . One can teach doctors: "On the basis of our experiment on animals, we feel that such-and-such techniques are indicated in such-and-such cases." Let them experiment then on human beings. And if your techniques don't work, you can always explain this away. "You should have approached this on the basis of accumulative experience, Comrades. One can't blindly transpose laboratory indications into clinical practice." Mothers would no longer be coming to me with their tears. I'm a scientist! What do they understand about theory? All they want is the knife.

Of course, theory is an important field. Without those scientists, we could not cut into the lungs and patch up ventricle walls. Also, without them we would not be living in dread of the atom bomb which can tomorrow bury all our little Lenochkas. However, that is not the scientists' fault. But why not? They should have handled those matters with more thought, more care, instead of rushing blindly after beautiful mirages. They should not have been so overwhelmed by the seeming omnipotence of human genius.

I think I'm delving into a sphere which is foreign to me. Would I be able to restrain myself? They say mirages are fascinating. I don't know. I've never seen any.

No, pure science is not for me—medical science, I mean. I'm probably wrong, but I don't like it. Physiology is a fine thing, and experiments on animals are necessary. But the real satisfaction comes from watching results, from facing direct responsibility, from sharing joys and sorrows of all those mothers.

Again, high-sounding phrases.

And so I have gone far afield, and have returned to my starting point. There is just one course open to me—work. More surgery. I must learn more and teach other surgeons to work well and honestly.

No, that's not all. One must search. Science is very important. Real science, for people.

Now I'm going to bed. Officially going to bed. I'll take some luminal on top of the cognac.

Yes, I am going to bed. My Lenochka is already fast asleep. My wife and my daughter, Lisa, will go to bed just as soon as I turn off my light. I should go and say goodnight to them, let them think that I'm back to normal. But I'm not back to normal at all. In my subconscious I'm with those two families, in those two houses. What are they doing? Have they gone to bed, or are they still crying—two of them over the little coffin ready for tomorrow's funeral, and two in an empty house where their poor Mayachka seems still to be living? What can one say about that? Nothing.

Nothing.

The End of the First Day

The Second Day . . .

3

SIMA AND SHURA

For two years I haven't touched my book. Two years? Must be—almost to a day. It was also spring then. Late April or early May. I must learn to date my entries. I always leave out dates, even on letters.

Another spring.

The road leads uphill. I am going to the clinic. Almost every morning I climb this hill. And not only with my legs. With my thoughts, too. These morning walks are good for me. They give me a charge for the day.

The operation. I have a very difficult one to do today. Everything has been calculated and thought out hundreds of times, and I'm just looking at people, trees, cars. Even run through monologues in my mind. But all this is just on the surface of my brain. Deep inside, mentally, I am already in the operating room. The snatches of thoughts—*I must not forget* this. *Perhaps I'd better try it* this *way today. And if I discover* this, *I must stop. Wait. Discuss it with my assistants.* I even move my fingers a little in response to my thoughts.

Relax, Professor. Look around. What a beautiful day. A morning in May. The fragrance of apple blossoms. The first dawn of young leaves on the trees. The fleecy little clouds like gamboling lambs.

Words. Words are destructive—they fetter your thought. However, there must be words. A writer's talent, it seems, is to express feelings with words. No, he must know how to feel also. How simple and pleasant this must be: to dream, feel, describe.

I can't afford feelings today. Perhaps that's why I don't admire this beautiful morning. No, my friend, it's much simpler: you're just blind. And yet, as I remember, I used to like to watch sunrises and sunsets. Yes, long ago, before the war. For me the war has never really ended.

Usually, during my morning walks I don't think about patients. I can control my thought, all the brakes are still holding fast. I think about operations, about the hearts and lungs, not people. About cases, but without faces. Without eyes.

But today I can't control myself too well. This is a very special day, a very risky operation on someone very close to me. Why the devil have I permitted him to become so close? Why have I spoken to him, delved into his soul? No, this is not correct, I have never reached his soul. Only his brain, his intellect. No, perhaps soul was there as well, but a very special soul, cold and dry, like a mathematical formula.

Careful, Professor! Don't let yourself go. This is dangerous. Breathe deeper, step livelier. All the sentiments were put to rest last night with a stiff dose of luminal.

But what about him? Has he slept well? It is important for him to have had a good rest. Emotions are mortal enemies of the heart. Even a healthy heart. But how can he approach this without emotion when he knows the truth? Others just trust you, they don't understand the situation, you can often deceive them.

But Sasha is a mathematician. He has calculated all odds, has taken into consideration all the chance factors.

Unfortunately, I'm not too sure about his calculations; I consider them too optimistic. I did not give him all the corrective coefficients; in fact, I don't know them myself any too well. In a number of areas I'm still guessing.

There is still time. I can call the operation off. I will examine him again, and decide then.

What a depressing case. Everything within me revolts against all those idiocies which compose life. Why all these sicknesses, quarrels, wars, oppressions? Again I'm asking stupid questions, just as I did two years ago. There are answers to all of them, or rather, the answers can be had. Sasha knew them all. Sasha again. After our talks, many things have become clear to me. I can't stop admiring his brain. Had he had good health and a little vanity, he could have accomplished great things. The word *health* sounds ironic today. His very life is hanging by the thinnest of threads.

I wish I could run through in my mind all our meetings, all our talks. I could always get so much strength out of them. I need it today.

My heart is in a painful vise.

No, I had better not. Once the operation is over, there will be time for this. The spring will unwind, the pressure will be off, there will be nothing to alter, nothing to mend. Then one can rummage through one's memories.

But now, step livelier. Walk faster. A surgeon must be alert, durable, lean.

All the preparations were completed yesterday. We even held a special meeting, just as we used to do years before, when we first experimented with our heart-lung AIK machine. The entire clinic is tense; Sasha is everyone's favorite. Probably everyone is thinking, Let's hope the Professor doesn't fly off the handle today. Not because they are afraid of insults, but they say I am losing my skill when I get excited. It sounds logical, but I haven't noticed it before. Must be my age, I suppose.

I won't swear today. I have no right to take chances.

Here it is, our home, our clinic. It looks handsome against the first pale green of the lindens. It should look good to people walking past it. But I can't see it that way. Suffering has colored it for me; to me it looks grim.

Two windows of the postoperation room. One of them is open and there is a vase on the sill with the first spring flowers. Behind them my imagination pictures different scenes which, alas, I know only too well. No, I'm going to drive those pictures out of my mind. There is no room for memories today. I must curb my emotion.

Benches. Relatives of our patients are already sitting there. They are always here except on bitterly cold days. Mothers of our children. Some happy, others unhappy. I walk past them with a frozen face. I can't force myself to smile this morning. Generally I don't like talking to relatives. I have enough tact and patience, but not enough human warmth. This, of course, is bad. But I must somehow defend myself from the anguish which seems to permeate this place. I can't live through their emotions. They are worried, but at least they are in good health. I must spare myself for the sick.

Just as I suspected. Sasha's wife is waiting for me, Raissa Sergeyevna, Raya for short. Probably a fine woman, but I didn't want to see her. Everything has been said, discussed, and there's nothing I can add. She doesn't appreciate the desperate state of her husband's health and is panic-stricken at the thought of the operation. Under such circumstances, I wouldn't have operated on any other patient. A patient even if he himself insists on surgery can die on the table, but his relatives remain and you can't explain anything, the surgeon is always a villain to them.

Very well. I'm not worrying about that now. I can't blame myself, because he himself demands surgery, and he knows the odds. My only problem is not to make any mistakes today.

"My dear Professor, will you operate today?"

"Good morning, Raissa Sergeyevna. Please calm yourself. You will need all your strength later on. Yes, I will operate, unless Sasha has changed his mind."

Tears.

"No, he hasn't. I've seen him. He wouldn't listen to me. Please refuse to operate, please!"

"I can't. As a physician I don't see an alternative. Without surgery he won't last a year."

"But he's not feeling too badly. Just a few days ago, he even went out on the balcony. The newspapers write about new preparations for rheumatism, perhaps they might help? Just suppose he dies today? What then?"

Yes, what then? I can't tell her that she is still young, that she would forget, and marry again. That she is perfectly able to take care of their son. And that the greatest loss would be not for her, but for science, for others. However, this is not really so; her loss would be irreplaceable, but science would find other Sashas.

"Raissa Sergeyevna, try to understand."

Now I deliver a short lecture on the nature of rheumatism, cardiac deficiencies, cirrhosis of the liver. Words which I have repeated at least twenty times. She can't understand me. She looks at me with her watery blue eyes. I am becoming gradually angry.

"Professor, wait at least another week. I beg you!"

"In a week it may be too late to do anything. Please forgive me, I'm in no mood for hysterics this morning. I must go."

I go. She is still trying to say something. No, I won't listen. That's all I need before a complicated operation! Let her go to hell. Deep inside, I'm sorry for her. She's unhappy, and this is not her fault. Nobody's fault. Or rather, our common fault, for not being able to create life without such dramas, terrible dramas claiming people's lives.

I still have a few minutes before our morning conference. I must go and see him.

The third floor. A small private ward. Flowers. Sasha is sitting up in his bed. A hunched posture, a mournful expression. Pitiful. I'm terribly sorry for him.

"Ah, Professor, good morning! Come in, come in!"

He smiles. A beautiful, radiant smile on the thin gray face. I look at him for a moment, both as a doctor and as a friend. He seems to be bearing up well.

"Slept well, my boy?"

Usually I am not this familiar with him. I call him Alexander Nikolayevich. After all he is not a boy, but a scientist, a man of refined intelligence and fine manners. He calls all the orderlies by their patronymics. But today this is different. I must get through to him, must give him a boost. His Raya, of course, has already been here and has done her best to unnerve him.

"Stay a minute, Professor."

I force a cheerful smile and sit down facing him.

Suddenly he becomes serious. "We have but little time. You must attend your morning conference and Dmitry Alexeyevich is already waiting for me with his needles. First, about the operation. We shall do what we have decided to do. The only thing that remains to me is to bear it like a man. I will try."

"Everything will be all right. I am sure."

I am not sure at all. But I have already said everything I could last night. Once he has decided, he will not change his mind. So I might as well lie.

"No, Professor. I like logic, and my logic works well, despite all the emotional pressures. I have detained you not to be comforted. You have done a great deal for me, you are a man who—"

"Please, Sasha—no big words! I don't like them." I think this is the first time that I have called him Sasha, and it seems to me that he has liked that.

He reaches under his pillow and brings out a thick school notebook.

"I have a manuscript here. A brief digest of my ideas about which I have spoken to you. There are a few new points, the result of the last few days. Please read this at leisure. I'm not looking for recognition, but it will be—would be pleasant to me if my thoughts should prove to be interesting . . . to someone. This is number one. The second point, Serezha, my son. You know my wife, Raya. I'm not going to speak about her now. I know that you won't be able to influence my son's upbringing, this is technically impossible, even if you'd want to do it. But in a few years he will understand many things he doesn't understand today, and I ask you . . . speak to him then about life and about myself. And about my work."

He hands the notebook to me. His hand trembles a little. His eyes are thoughtful and just a little moist. A pause.

"Now, there's still another thing. Here's a letter. In all probability a woman will come to see you, very soon. Read this letter yourself, and then give it to her, under any circumstances. Be sure to read it first, then you will know how to speak to her. And if by any chance I survive—well, we'll simply forget about this and won't mention it again. I suppose that is all."

He smiles again, his usual wonderful smile. This time, almost a happy smile.

"I could talk to you forever, Professor, but there's no time. And your drugs didn't work very well. My head is completely clear."

"You have a different head, Sasha. When you get well, we shall construct a special machine to regulate advanced brain kitchens. Then the next mathematician will sleep like a baby before his operation and have some fine scientific dreams."

A rather childish phrase. I try to laugh, and he does the same. Then he glances at his wristwatch.

"You'd better go, Professor. So long, and I wish you all the luck in the world today."

What he probably means is "Goodbye." He knows that I feel the same way. We can't fool each other.

I get up. I am relieved that I can leave. People are all the same.

"All right, Sasha, don't worry too much. No use going through long goodbyes, we'll see each other tonight. Keep it up, don't let science down."

He smiles again, makes a slight parting gesture. I believe he has been cheered up a little, and all of a sudden I also feel better. There is great salutary power in a joke and a smile. Even under such conditions.

It is already five minutes past nine. I'm five minutes late for the conference. Let's hope we all live through this.

Morning conferences in our clinic are an important part of our work. True, they take time, but this is time well spent.

A hall. A single table, large enough for a presidium, but I alone sit at it. Behind me is a large X-ray projection screen. Rows of chairs. In the first row, my senior assistants, the anesthetist, Maria Vasilievna, Petro, Semyon Ivanovich, Oleg. Behind them, the interns, and still further, nurses. There are many people here; some girls have to stand up at the back. It is not too quiet here either; people like to talk.

We have a certain routine. First, night nurses give their reports: so many patients, so many in good condition, so many dangerously ill—unfortunately there are always enough of those. In about fifteen minutes, the nurses leave for the wards. Then the surgeons who did operations on the previous day describe them to us: what was discovered, what was done, complications, the state of the patients in the morning. All mistakes are discussed openly and honestly. They say that this is a unique procedure we have. "Criticism and self-criticism, regardless of personalities." I have long since come to the conclusion that to hide one's mistakes is simply impractical; they will become known anyway and will be blown up by gossip. Of course, it is not too pleasant to speak about one's mistakes when there are forty people in the room; the whole town learns about them, but we accept that. This is an extremely useful practice.

Then the physician on night duty makes his report:

"There are one hundred and forty-five patients in the clinic. On the third floor there is a serious case, a woman called Trofimchuk. Asthma, shortness of breath. She's in an oxygen tent. Pulse one hundred and forty, arrhythmia. The general picture is of terminal decompensation. In the postoperative ward the condition of all patients is satisfactory."

A momentary pause, then:

"The second floor. A serious case, Onipko, one lung removed on account of cancer. Accumulation of air in the remaining lung, I have pumped it out several times from the pleura. There were signs of asphyxiation, but now his condition is more satisfactory. I found his blood pressure rising and have been administering Pentamin."

I hear Petro whisper under his breath, "What a liar, what a bastard!" Then, aloud:

"Stepan Stepanovich, what do you mean, 'more satisfactory'? He might die at any minute. Better tell us how you have set up the air pump."

Stepan Stepanovich hesitates. I demand a clarification from Petro.

"I don't know what Stepan has been doing with the patient during the night, but this morning I found Onipko blue, gasping for air and with a high blood pressure: a clinical picture of acute oxygen hunger. The pump was not working because it hadn't been set up correctly, and the lung was packed. I reset the pump, inserted a tube into the trachea and pumped out a great deal of sticky phlegm. He is feeling better now, the blood pressure has gone down to normal, but he has been a long time in a state of oxygen deficiency, and this might affect his heart most dangerously."

I assume a frozen expression. Scenes like this are not unusual with us and they are never treated on a personal basis. In fact, Petro and Stepan Stepanovich are good friends. But with us, our work comes first.

I take over. "Do you know how to operate the pump, Stepan Stepanovich?"

"Yes, I know."

"How many times did you check it during the night?"

He answers, many times; but I know he is lying.

"Did you examine the patient?"

"Yes, I did."

"And—?"

Silence. A new question, seemingly a casual one:

"Why did Onipko's blood pressure go up?"

A pause. Then: "I know now that it was due to oxygen hunger, but I thought it was a simple case of natural hypertension."

"Too bad you have discovered this only now."

Another pause. Dead silence in the room. I am thinking, What an idiot. What is he doing here? However, I must be polite. I speak calmly:

"Stepan Stepanovich. The whole thing is clear to me and I don't want any explanations. You will have to leave the clinic because you are not fit to do the kind of work we are doing here. Let me remind you that when you were accepted, we informed you about our conditions. If we found you unsuited, I was to tell you so, and you were to start looking for another position and then resign without any black mark against your record. By the same token, if you found our way of working unsuitable for you, you were free to leave at any moment, even if you were a genius and we needed you desperately. This is no reflection upon your professional ability, our standards are exacting and only a few doctors can meet them. Let me also remind you that you have already had two serious warnings. Also, once before, I suggested that you resign; you promised to do so, but have never come around to doing it. The first time I chose to overlook it, but now I must insist. Human life is irreplaceable, and we can't experiment with it, forgive me for this banal statement."

A slight pause, then:

"Let me repeat again for the benefit of everyone here: This clinic has its own code applicable to the entire personnel. We all work as much and as hard as is required by the situation. No set hours, no overtime computation, no side benefits, we start on time and go home only when our work is done. The second rule: Should any worker prove to be unsuited to our standards, he must leave on his own. The question of unsuitability is decided by me, but since it is human to err, I consult my senior assistants. Your case, Stepan Stepanovich, was discussed about six months ago, and it was agreed that you would be asked to leave if you made another error. Therefore, unless you resign now, I'll have no alternative but to ask for your dismissal through official channels. There is no dearth of opportunities for a surgeon in this town, but this clinic needs a special kind of people with a special kind of dedication. So?"

Stepan Stepanovich stands there looking miserable.

"Very well, I'll resign. But give me time to find another place. . . . I have a family."

"How much time?"

Silence. Oppressive silence.

"You have two weeks. Sit down."

Perhaps this is cruel. I can see that everyone is ill at ease and ashamed. To dismiss a physician like this! But what can one do in such cases? The man is at fault. He pretty nearly killed a patient. This is not the first time he has made this same mistake: six months ago a little boy died during his shift under almost identical circumstances, Stepan failed to pump out phlegm. But I'm still sorry for the young man. Perhaps I should have had another heart-to-heart talk with him? Tried to influence him, to help him? Given him some more time? No, enough. What would I have told Onipko's daughter?

Suddenly Petro gets up:

"Professor, let's keep Stepan on. He will be more careful from now on."

Petro has himself raised the fuss, and now he wants to be charitable.

"You want to keep him on? Very well, I agree. If you will stand his shifts and care for his patients. Let him just draw his salary."

How insulting this is! Stepan turns red, rises and leaves the room. I pretend I haven't noticed it. Everyone hates me at this moment, even those who voted for his dismissal six months before. I feel it.

Petro is still standing. "Please forgive him, Professor. We will help him. He's a good doctor. Is that right, Comrades?"

There is a hum of supporting voices.

All I can do is keep silent. A very unpleasant episode. But I just can't act otherwise. They all think I'm cruel. But I think just the contrary. I'm helping Stepan to find his proper place in society. Not every doctor can work under our conditions. No, not many even. And still I feel sorry, but I must control my emotion. Let it lie for a while.

"Let's have the report on today's surgery."

The detailed discussion on all patients booked for surgery each week is held every Saturday. The schedules are set then too. Each morning the surgeons just remind everyone of the operations for the day and discuss the surgical plans. Some of these discussions are quite time-consuming, we welcome all suggestions, all criticism.

Today is a typical day: five operations, one with artificial blood circulation, Sasha. As a rule we begin with lighter cases. Two interns tell us about their stenosis cases. Then, a case of lung cancer. Semyon will again sew up the prenatal channel between the aorta and lung artery in a boy who was first operated on two years ago, just before the tragic case of Maya. I remember too well that dead girl on the table. It is best not to think about *that,* now.

Since then we have changed our methods. We now close the opening with double sutures and also with a wire clamp. But in four previous cases there were recurrences requiring secondary surgical interference. Fortunately, without aneurysms.

A lot of water has flowed under the bridge since those days. We have advanced greatly. When we say "we," we mean our clinic. Outwardly this can be noticed by the volume of surgery and a number of previously inoperable cases being operated on. But behind all this lies work and research into the nature of the human body, of ills besetting it.

Our physicians have also advanced. Semyon will today do secondary surgical repair which once only I and Maria Vasilievna could do successfully. Petro is already a doctor of science. He and Maria Vasilievna are now casually performing surgery with the AIK heart-lung machine. Ten candidates are sitting before me right now. True, they don't appear to me more intelligent than they were before, but when I read their papers I know that they have been doing a lot of work in their chosen fields.

Our AIK machine is not the machine we used at first. It is still not absolutely perfect, not to the point of perfection that would completely satisfy us. But we can disconnect the heart now for two or three hours at a stretch and hemolysis stays within tolerable limits. This is good. But it is possible to do this better still, and the engineers are working on new models. We can also use AIK as a supplementary apparatus in lighter cases for many hours without ill effects on patients. There are other new developments as well.

Yes, our renown has grown, too. Our clinic has a widespread reputation. People speak about miracles which we allegedly perform here. Everyone looks at the outward appearances, but only very few know what all this has cost us. When I spoke about our standards, I didn't exaggerate, we are driving ourselves to the very limits. Still, I would have gladly exchanged my fame and all my honorary degrees for just one thing: the lower mortality rate of our patients. Yes—honestly? Yes.

They will now report on Sasha. (We did not discuss his case last Saturday because we did not know then that we would operate on him.) Of course, I have discussed it many times with the senior physicians, but the routine must be adhered to; every case must be presented to all the doctors and all suggestions considered. Especially because all of them know and like him. And perhaps they will stop being annoyed with me for my dismissal of Stepan after they hear my plan.

Vasya reports on the case clinically, but before my eyes this story presents itself differently, with all my emotions and painful doubts.

"The patient Popovsky, Alexander Nikolayevich, thirty-two, mathematician, doctor of sciences, was admitted to the clinic four months ago with a diagnosis of insufficiency of the heart valve. In the course of the last two years he has been admitted three times to this clinic, and twice into other hospitals. The general condition is that of a rapid circulatory deterioration. Pulse one hundred and ten with twinkling arrhythmia . . ."

Now come the findings of various analyses. The X rays show the enlargement of all sections of the heart. Final diagnosis: chronic insufficiency of the heart valve with large deposits of lime. Impeded blood circulation. Considerable secondary changes in the liver. The indication, immediate radical surgery.

I personally present the surgery plan. Opening of the left pleural area, then the pericardium. Artificial blood circulation. Hypothermia, the artificial cooling of the body. Incision of the left auricular area. The examination of the valve. If the folds are not too badly degenerated, an attempt to perform plastic correction. If that does not appear to be possible, then removal and insertion of an artificial valve. This technique, if successful, would immediately correct insufficiency and facilitate heart action. This has been proved on the test stand.

There are no questions and no suggestions. The junior doctors probably do not feel entitled to question me, and the seniors have been fully briefed by me in advance.

My supporting team: Maria Vasilievna, and two young surgeons, Eugene and Vasya. The anesthetist, Dima, that is, Dmitry Alexeyevich.

The conference is over. People leave silently. I know that most of them did not like my treatment of Stepan. I don't feel too happy myself about it, but I can't let that bother me. All my thoughts are about the operation. Stepan's hurt pride is insignificant compared with that. He will live through it. Let him work somewhere else and not hurt *my* patients. This is how I argue with myself. He's erred, he must pay for it. The sense of retribution is deeply ingrained in human nature. All right. I must suppress all this for a while. I can do it and I will. I must concentrate on the operation.

I will go to my office, sit down and think a while. I must pull myself together. Inside.

My office. Such a cold bare place. Somehow I don't know how to create pleasant surroundings. Well, to hell with them. I am dying for a cigarette, but I don't dare to smoke. Before important operations I try to abstain. Nicotine blurs the brain, and makes my hands tremble more than usual.

What shall I do now? They will probably take an hour or so getting everything ready, assembling materials, instruments, nurses and doctors, preparing the patient. I can't bring order into this; I have tried and failed. They say there are clinics working with absolute precision. If an operation is booked for nine, it starts at nine. I can only envy them.

My desk is covered with papers, but most of them are either unpleasant or uninteresting. Dissertations sent in for criticism. Scientific papers of our kids. Numerous letters from relatives of patients who can't be operated on because their cases have been judged inoperable. How can I answer them? I have no time for protracted explanations. And there are not the right kind of words for this. Ah, here's a pleasant letter! I have read it before, but I want to read it again. From Katya's mother. What was her name? She had sclerosis. Oh yes, the name was Sadovaya! "Dear Professor: Yesterday was the first anniversary of the operation. We are celebrating this occasion more than her birthday." Very warming. We had had some very hard times with her before we succeeded in saving her.

Let me look at Sasha's case history once again. It is a long one, a whole thick folder.

Analysis. X rays. Entries. And along with them, the real story. Not the one which is written down in this folder, but the one which only I know so well. Everything is intermingled here: Sasha, his work, his sickness, my own emotions, surgery.

Can it be that I have made a radical mistake proposing the valvulotomy and the possible insertion of an artificial heart valve?

I am not thinking with words. I know this story so well that I don't need them. Various pictures race through my mind. Long conversations are condensed into brief sense digests; they pass by with lightninglike rapidity. When one speaks or writes, one drags along an ever-growing burden of words; many of them heavy, cumbersome, inexpressive, unnecessary. Will there ever come a time when people will be able to communicate without words? Fantasy. They say that mental telepathy occurs between people very close to each other. "Understanding without words." Have I ever experienced it? No, probably not. This is something very primitive.

I am not feeling well at all. A feeling of gnawing uneasiness. Probably this sort of thing occurs to war leaders, before some decisive battle.

Our first meeting. Some three years ago. It was in an X-ray laboratory during ambulatory hours. Many patients. A good-looking young man sent in with a mitral stenosis.

"There is no stenosis. The cardiac insufficiency is of the third degree."

Those therapeutists very often send in patients with wrong diagnoses. Even now. However, one must not criticize them; it is the most difficult branch of medicine, working by guess and mental deduction. It calls for extreme intelligence besides experience.

A soft, pleasant voice, fine choice of words. Timid questions.

The verdict: "You must wait. We are still at the exploratory stage in this field."

Of course, what could I offer him then? Had we made our first bungling surgical attempts in that sphere then? I'm beginning to forget chronology. How is it possible to forget such things?

Yes, there had been some surgical pioneering in the cases of insufficiency even then. I had experimented myself. I can remember it plainly. Bleeding. Fibrillation. Death on the table. The feeling of emptiness and anger. "A pioneer indeed. Bungler!"

Can the same thing happen today? I can see myself coming home. "Dammit all to hell! No more valves! I'll stitch up hernias and take out appendices from now on! I'm quitting! I'm through!"

Too bad moments like that become forgotten. You cool off, recover, try again, grow too confident, make mistakes. Anyway, I could offer Sasha nothing then, not even hope. Insufficiency patients just had to wait. Tragically, with death coming nearer every day.

Sasha left, but he came back to us. In six months or so, I think. We were already working on new techniques. The AIK machine was not used on humans then, only dogs. It means that this was more than three years ago. How time flies! Let it fly. I don't want to either stop it or turn it back, I don't want anything. Of course, this is just a momentary reaction to my present anguish. If the operation is successful, I'll be as cocky as ever. "Bring them on! I'm just starting!"

I was in one of these expansive moods when Sasha came back. I was sitting in this office, after a successful operation. (Esophagus, I think. Such a funny old man. He got well.) A feeling of relaxation. A wonderful taste of tobacco smoke in my mouth. (If I could only have one puff now!) I was in no hurry. I examined Sasha at length. Then he still had a thin layer of fat in his stomach; now all this is gone and only the hard liver is pushing its way out. I remember that his personality struck me as even more pleasant than during the first visit. I told him about our work on the new operation. Why? Just to brag, I suppose. But he caught fire, not realizing that all my words were mere wishful thinking. I didn't realize it myself, then. So we went on, further and further. The general conversation about medicine, the nature of it, experimental probing without a firm theory, by touch, by trial and error, by guess and inspiration. Not really a precise science. Then we spoke about a diagnostic machine, there were items in the press about it just then, and we at the clinic had become interested. Sasha was overwhelmed by the idea and offered his services as a mathematician. I remember a thought passing through my mind then: *Such a pleasant and intelligent young man, and yet his condition will deteriorate, and there is nothing anyone can do about it. Shall I discourage him right now, tell him the truth? Oh, never mind!*

Now this "never mind" has come home to roost.

Had I told him the truth then, sent him away, I would not be sitting here now in such a miserable state.

It would have been helpful to have some of those medical machines now. One for the automatic regulation of the heart-lung machine, for instance. Those girl operators make mistakes now and then, and today it will be especially difficult.

Sasha did not go seriously into that work, he had switched to psychology. Too bad. Perhaps we could have had something today which we could have used in his case.

Today our AIK machine will work for at least an hour and a half. Will it be possible to maintain the constancy of all the blood components? The least sign of oxygen hunger would mean the end in his case. He would never survive it.

What an interesting man! I had been completely overwhelmed by him after we had met for a few times. That was our "honeymoon." It is a pity our relationship went sour, and never reverted to its original closeness. The true warmth had been lost. Had he ever felt it toward me? I don't know.

He had opened for me an entirely new world of

abstract thinking. What was the essence of his theory? The quantitative correlation in everything. "The informative plan of the universe." I can't explain it in words—not competent enough, and anyway Sasha had invented his own set of terms. It covers everything, biology, arts, social sciences. Everywhere the same law of "information digestion and assimilation." I'd better not try to define it accurately. Only he could assort all those things in precise categories and evolve his theories, some precise, some still vague.

And soul? This I don't know. I'm often at a loss to define this word. I often make mistakes in evaluating people on this basis. He had an open smile, gentleness, impeccable tact, courtesy. A complete absence of vanity. Never a censoring word about anyone. Now it seems to me that beneath it all there was a kind of quiet sense of superiority, of detachment. Wisdom or emotional poverty?

Are we good friends? I—yes, but what about him? We used to meet every week. As a doctor I could see his deterioration. He had difficulty in breathing and was always tired. He used to lie down during our discussions, after thousands of excuses, which always angered me. He could not be really simple. Was this the result of his genteel upbringing or some innate reserve? I was always a little upset by this. Well, may God help him, one can't judge him today. He is about to mount his Golgotha. (Sounds very stilted.)

Have they taken him up yet? It's ten-thirty, about time. He was smiling so easily today. But what will it be in a few hours? How should I bear his death? (I should have taken Stepan Stepanovich aside and dismissed him privately, not in front of the whole clinic.)

I can remember the operation for which I was preparing when Sasha and I really met. I was sure it would be successful, such stupid confidence. The patient died within a few days from cardiac weakness. My repair job on his heart valve was sloppy. "This is the last time! Never again! Let them die without me!"

Sasha too was upset over my failure. Soon there appeared signs of decompensation in him, and we had to admit him into the clinic. He used to write all the time, in bed. "There's so little time left, and I have to solve so many things. I'd like to understand them myself. I know I won't have enough time to convey them to others in any event."

He was an omnivorous reader, books on Yoga, the Bible, on telepathy, on ESP. But he did not become a mystic; he made fun of mysticism. "There's nothing to it, just an excuse for insufficient knowledge. The whole world is just a machine."

Machine? Consciously and intellectually I have never believed in God, and yet I feel uneasy when they threaten to reduce all human feelings to computer equations. I want to think that their machine feelings will not be true feelings. Not quite real. But Sasha is absolutely convinced. He says that all emotions can be reduced to mathematics, and that they will be true and real.

I remember the magnificent feeling of elation after our first successful operation with the AIK machine. Could a feeling like this be reproduced mechanically? I don't know. Of course I trust Sasha, I don't question his theories, but perhaps I am too old to start worshiping any new gods. A conventional materialism is enough for me, with its "qualitative differentiations" between the physical and the psychic. And as to cybernetics, I am completely satisfied with the idea of a diagnostic computer and an apparatus regulating the artificial blood circulation. They don't need any feelings.

And what about conscience, for instance? Can a machine have it?

However, I acted childishly quarreling with him. Friendship is a sacred thing, it can't be toyed with and discarded like a used blood swab. I was insulted if you please, outraged.

Yes, I was wrong, but was our friendship mutual? I should not question this now. Everyone gives just as much as he can. He couldn't give more than he did. With him, everything had gone into intellect. Also, he was a sick man. It was during his second stay with us, if I remember correctly. Yes, the second.

It was a difficult period for me, our first failures. We thought that with the artificial blood circulation, we could correct insufficiency. And then, fatalities. First one, then others. I was in the dumps.

Really, Sasha was not very sensitive. He should not have attacked me when I came to him as a friend seeking help, crushed, destroyed. And instead, he showed me an American magazine with photographs of artificial heart valves. I shrugged them off—a couple of experimental operations, nothing conclusive at all. I was wrong, of course. We had fallen behind and that was our fault. We hadn't worked hard enough, had not tried to overcome all obstacles. "To overcome obstacles." Sounds like propaganda.

What exactly had he told me?

"Well, it seems I won't last long enough until *you* catch up with real science."

It was the way he said that. Here am *I,* and there are *you.* He was then working on something very important for defense, solving some difficult problem, and it was a race against time. And we could not perform an operation which had already been done elsewhere!

What could I tell him?

But why dwell upon it now, why remember? He was a sick man. He was doing important work, and yet he felt that his life was nearing an end. And he saw all the mediocrities around him bungling things away, things which he knew how to do correctly. Enough to make even the most tactful man bitter.

And what about our friendship?

Of course I acted like a spoiled child when I did not go back to him, but he also made no effort to approach me. And how much had I been longing for some little move from his side!

All right, let's forget it. It's all forgotten, almost forgotten. And today I stand in a noble posture. "You have turned away from me, but I have proved myself. And I don't even expect appreciation." Yes, somewhere, in the back alleys of my mind, there is a thought like this, "I have proved myself." What have I proved? Two artificial valves, one fatality. And I did not develop the valve itself; it was Misha Savchenko who had made it. Have I made any mistakes inserting them? Yes, Shura. Our nurses buried her.

But today I shall fight like a demon. I won't let anything slip through my fingers. Or else, I shall really quit, once and for all.

Also, one operation was a success. Sima. Sima, Simochka! This very name is like honey to me. Just like my own daughter.

I remember when I first saw her. A ward inspection. A pretty girl. The look: suffering, hope, fear. It is impossible to describe that look. Insufficiency with acute decompensation. Had been in different hospitals for almost a year. Knows everything. If I refuse, the end.

What could I tell her? If the valve folds are in a good state, something can be done, but what if there are lesions and lime deposits? Then nothing can be done short of removing the valve and replacing it with an artificial one, a wildly speculative attempt. True, Misha had already constructed the valve, a good one. But all the dogs on whom we had experimented died. It seemed that healthy hearts rejected it, we had to hope that hearts in morbid condition would assimilate them; nature works this way sometimes. But we had had no experience, and I did not know how long it would be before we mastered this technique. After that, months of postoperative observation to make sure that the results were lasting. At least a year. Much too long for her.

"Professor, I beg you, don't refuse!"

"We will see."

My office. Her parents, a middle-aged couple. I was completely frank with them. I told them that I was scared to death, that I did not want to accept responsibility.

"Save her! We trust you. You are our only hope."

Those words cut me like a knife, "trust, hope." Well, there was no hope; she was doomed. Surgery was the only answer, perhaps a negative one, but still an answer. And so I agreed. And succeeded.

Sasha says the same thing: "Please go ahead. I have nothing to lose." No one wants to understand that I also lose something. (No, Simochka, with you I lost nothing, I found a great deal!)

But what about Shura?

Will it be the same thing with Sasha? God, they are namesakes. "There is nothing. Just a machine."

I remember Sima's operation. I had planned it as a plastic valve correction. The artificial blood circulation. Temperature down to twenty degrees. The heart has stopped. I am opening it up. Terrible! The valve folds are full of lesions. I'm trying a plastic approach, completely hopeless. All I can do is to sew the mess up. I know the heart won't ever start up again. Emotions. I am damning everything and everybody, myself, my assistants, surgery, the patient. "I know you will surely save me." I wish everything around me would go to hell. But oaths and emotions help nothing, I must stitch up the wound. Without hope. This is like working on a corpse.

Suddenly someone suggests: "Let's put in Misha's valve. What can we lose?"

A storm of thoughts. Shall I try? If the valve does not take, she will die later on, not now. This is better. And if——? The valve is good, it had been tested on the stand. And if a failure? Whispers: "They are experimenting on people without sufficient preliminary experience." And—who knows?—perhaps even an official inquiry. If I leave her like this, no one can blame me; "the case proved to be inoperable." Oh, to hell with it!

"Bring it in, quickly!"

It had fitted well, and I inserted it cleanly. The operation is over. She wakes up. The heart works beautifully. Everyone is happy. Except me. I feel like a charlatan when I smile. I know that the valve is attached with sutures which will dissolve in a week or two. What then?

What days I had! Every morning I would run straight to her and listen to the heart. "Please don't worry, I feel fine." It was she who would try to calm me down. So funny.

How will I handle all this today? I would have felt so much surer if not for my second case, Shura. I must cut the auricular area wider than I did for her and then I can see the valve better. Of course, the stitching up will be more difficult, but that doesn't matter, the most important thing is to have enough room to work in.

Whatever one may say, there is more hope now; we know definitely that an artificial valve can be successfully inserted. Sima has been alive for three months, and there are no signs of any complications. We don't have to experiment on dogs any longer.

The thing one must guard against is embolism. No, I won't let this happen today. What an idiot I was to let it happen to Shura, I was too excited, too sure of myself. The valve in her case seemed to have fitted even better than Sima's. All right, let's not remember. Let's think about Sasha.

How pitiful he looked when he came to us this time. A pale face, swollen legs, the liver almost up to the navel. The clinical picture of a terminal case. I was so ashamed of myself because of our quarrel. Now all this is gone, we seem to have made peace. I have redeemed my guilt.

"Professor, here I am again. Just try to keep me going for as long as you can."

"Nonsense, Alexander Nikolayevich. Everything will

be all right. You will stay with us for a month or two, then, back to work."

"Not any longer. My status is that of invalid, and anyway—all I need is a couple of months more. I must finish some work."

We put him in a private ward. Started to treat him with everything we had. My kids are really remarkable, they can handle difficult cases like seasoned veterans. Especially Maria Vasilievna. Every doctor should be like her. If she could only find time to write her dissertation.

At that time I was still not quite sure about Sima. Only two weeks after the operation. I was waiting for a disaster. I had recurring nightmares, I'm coming into the ward and find her with blue lips, gasping for air. The fear of death in her eyes. Those looks!

But our doctors and nurses were already full of confidence. Our first valve, not a joke! We also knew something and could show those foreigners a thing or two.

Perhaps this atmosphere worked well on Sasha. He started to feel better. Psychology is an important factor.

I wish my own psychology were better today. If it were not for Shura. But no, that case proves nothing. Just a stupid oversight. Today I'll watch every second, all the way. Like a machine.

"Put in a valve!"

Sasha started to say this a week after admission. "Put in a valve!" So easy to say! But the idea started to circulate among our people, and gradually I have accepted it too. After all, Sima was doing so well, a whole month after the operation. It was a chance for Sasha; without it he had none.

He is probably being taken into surgery now. The second round of medications must now be taking hold.

There are certain preparations for suppression of fear and anxiety. They inhibit emotion.

He is fully aware of his condition. He knows me well. He knows that my hands tremble and that I get excited during surgery. He knows that there are many questionable factors which will become apparent only during the operation. (I feel a little ashamed of myself and my medicine.)

We had spoken a great deal of late, after he started to feel better. He even used to come here and sit in that chair. (How comfortable these modern chairs are.)

I tried hard to understand him.

"I have no choice. I have read everything, and I know it all. Also I'm tired. I can't start any serious work, because I won't have enough time to finish it. This is like living at an airport, the flight has been delayed, but it will take off without fail. Of course, I'm continuing to think, but this is just a momentum. Actually, I have completed one stage of my work. I understand the basic principles of the laws governing action of cell, individual, society. The next step is to prove it, to fight for it. This is already a job for a whole collective. If I survive, we shall start."

Then, on another occasion:

"Put in a valve and I'll describe to you the entire pattern of human behavior with differential equations."

But his soul I could not reach. Was it just his outward manner, or the absence of what we call a soul? The Raja-Yoga, "accomplishment through knowlege"? Or is he just a man obsessed by his own hypotheses?

"Put in a valve. I shall die anyway, so what's the difference? One month sooner, one month later."

Yes, what's the difference? If he were a man in love

with life, he would have fought for every extra day. Just to live till the spring, to smell the linden buds again. But Sasha lives outside that sort of time.

It is all the same to him, but what about me? If he dies, what would I tell myself? Without surgery he might live perhaps another year. But this would be slow dying. Without sleep, with asthma, with swellings. And there won't be any choice then, nothing to decide. Today he can still decide. Not alone, of course, but with me, *only* with me. This is not a routine operation where if one surgeon refuses you go to another.

Are you already looking for an alibi, my friend? It won't help. Death is death, and you would be the direct cause of it.

Why do I go through all this, now? It's too late. He is already in the operating room. Dima is injecting Tiopental, and Sasha is going to sleep. What are his last thoughts? No one will ever know. (Why had this stupid thing with Stepan Stepanovich happened this morning? Why not tomorrow?)

I had tried to resist.

"Let's wait a while. Let's make sure that Sima's valve has really taken root. Then let me try once again."

"No, I want to be next!"

"We must try first on an easier case. Your liver is in bad shape, we need time to tune it up."

I had hoped to do two or three operations before coming to him.

But where would I get such two or three easy cases? Really easy cases don't need artificial valves.

Every serious patient insists on an immediate operation. Regardless of risk. But I know that the risk is much too great, at least eighty per cent, or more. I was simply lucky with Sima. After a few fatalities, it would be impossible even to offer this kind of surgery. Try to prove that the case was really inoperable. Impossible, even to yourself.

Sima has been living for three months and improving. The valve has undoubtedly been integrated. Theoretically I can start on others. I always have suitable cases on hand. All I have to do is to choose one and schedule surgery. That's how it appears from the outside. Why not take a light case with obvious insufficiency, but without decompensation?

In practice this is not so easy. You can't go to a patient and tell him: "I'm going to insert an artificial valve into your heart, and you will get well." Everyone of them would grab at this opportunity. And then, if it is a failure, what are you supposed to tell their relatives?

"But, Professor, you said, you promised."

Every patient would know about it. It would undermine all confidence.

Again, and it is the main point, I am ashamed to lie. I haven't learned to use human lives as experimental material. I've been doing it all my life, but I've never got used to it.

Then there's another terrible thought, and it comes easy to people: "He likes to do spectacular surgery, looking for glory." And the devil of it is that there is a grain of truth in it. "I shall be the first one to insert an artificial valve. I shall make a report to the Society, publish a paper. The newspapermen will clamor to see me." I am trying to drive these thoughts away, but they are very persistent. And I fear them desperately, superstitiously. I have noticed this many times. Comes an interesting patient. You begin to think about an unusual operation for him, honestly, to save his life. But this terrible thought already stirs in the back of your mind: "I will write a paper, publish it." You perform the operation. The patient dies. Anger. Mental flagellation. Despair. "I'm a monster! I killed a man to write a paper!"

I am dying for a smoke!

What will happen today? For the hundredth time I'm reviewing the whole thing in my mind. The most dangerous and least-known element, the liver. I'm going through all the analyses again. Here, at the admission. Very bad. The next one, a seeming improvement. This one, a marked improvement. Here one can actually consider surgery. (It was during this period that I made my promise to operate.)

And now, this one. An almost catastrophic deterioration. Just one day after Shura's operation!

What terrible days those were.

Shura. I will never forget her. She was a sad case, all alone, incapable of work, living in a communal house. "I might as well die." I tried to be scrupulously honest. Perhaps too honest. I explained everything to her, quoted the odds. Told her that she would probably live a few years longer with her own valve, bad as it was. I practically prepared her for death and let her choose.

That was cruel. But I have no strength any longer to decide about human lives. I know that those humane and strong people say, "A doctor must assume the entire responsibility and has no right to involve the patient in his decision, to give him a psychological trauma." Some even add: "This goes for relatives as well." But where would you get moral strength to decide for everyone?

Shura had no one. Probably I should have assumed

full responsibility in her case and not frightened her. Even lied, if necessary. At least she would have gone onto the table with more confidence. And why did I select her? To get some additional experience before Sasha's operation, or because she had no relatives? No, I truly wanted to save her. She seemed a fairly good risk.

I don't want to remember that day, but I must. So that it won't be repeated today.

Almost certainly in Shura's case the draining tube out of the ventricle had not been properly adjusted after we had checked on the valve function. The machinists claim that everything had been done correctly. It is impossible to determine this now. But the fact remains, air embolism of the brain vessels. She did not wake up.

How I am going to fear this moment today, the awakening. In Shura's case the valve was inserted quite well, everyone could see that during the autopsy.

Today I won't permit embolism under any circumstance. We will insert a thick draining tube into the ventricle and pump the blood out for ten, even twenty minutes! We won't allow a single air bubble to get into the blood stream. I can see this tube filled with steady-flowing blood. I can almost feel it.

Mistakes. Mistakes. Can one learn to treat people without them? Sasha says this is impossible without machines. The human system is so complicated that the brain can't fully grasp the entire correlation of elements in it. Only machines can compute and organize all this information for instant use. But I don't think I'll live long enough to see this.

If no embolism, then there might be something else. There is no end to surprises in a difficult case like this one. We just haven't had enough experience. Empty worries. Nothing can be changed any longer.

How a single mistake can ruin everything!

At the time I operated on Shura, Sasha was in a fairly good state. After my fiasco he did not show any emotion at all; he appeared to be calm and as determined as ever. But both his heart and his liver slid back. Apparently he had not taken it so calmly, after all.

For as long as Shura was alive. ("Alive," a weird term to apply to a human being without a brain. No, enough of that!)

Her third day was especially difficult. No urine, asthma, she was barely alive. But Sasha repeated the same thing on that day: "Operate!" How could I operate in my state then, I felt like leaving it all and just running away. This wasn't the first time I had felt like that. But how could I abandon my patients? However, this is probably also a wrong argument: no one is indispensable and my assistants are very able.

Now, if he dies today.

I have done everything I could in this case to eliminate a basic diagnostic error, and to remove from myself the burden of arbitrary decision.

I held a general consultation with my colleagues, the best specialists in town. All the therapeutists agreed that the case was absolutely hopeless. That is, certain death, and a speedy one. Months perhaps, even weeks. At the same time I let them examine Sima. Not to boast, but to justify clinically my plans for surgery. But perhaps also to brag a little? Maybe. It is hard to say now.

The verdict was unanimous: immediate surgery indicated on the basis of previous clinical experience.

This means: Go and take your chance. Fine words.

Iron logic. If there is only a five-per-cent chance of success, the operation is indicated.

Therapeutists are generous with that sort of advice. I wish they would try to operate on the five-per-cent margin!

I would like to know who the bastard was who told Sasha about our concilium!

He looked at me with real anger next morning.

"I am master of my own life and you have no right to deprive me of even one per cent of hope!"

How defenseless we all are in the face of life! He demanded from me something which was incredibly difficult for me to do. But he had his point too. When even the slightest deterioration may mean death, one has no right to procrastinate and prepare alibis. But he should have expressed this differently. However, he apologized the next day and I forgot all about it.

"All right, we shall operate. But we must have a little time to build up your liver."

"How long?"

"Ten days."

My heart went into my mouth as I said it, and it has been there ever since. Even if the valve were to take, how long would it last? In Sasha's case, ten years would be a lifetime. Misha tells me that the materials have been thoroughly tested for lasting durability. But why look so far ahead? I must live through today first. Surgical mechanics and techniques develop so rapidly that within the next five years they might have something radically new that would change all today's estimates.

If I could only smoke! Just one draw. But no. I can't. I must be a machine.

Now the ten days have passed. And strange: just as soon as I made a firm promise, his condition began to improve. This means that there are some reserves in him. That is good.

It is interesting to know what he wrote in his notebook, and in the letter. Apparently there is a romance, or rather, *was*. Will it continue in the future? It's best not to think.

Now I must bid him a mental goodbye. In the operating theater there won't be any Sasha, just a body which can become a corpse. Something keeps me from opening his notebook. I can do this only *after*, whatever the outcome. Then I shall have the right. If he survives, he will become a sort of relative to me, a son. And if he dies, well, I have been appointed his trustee.

How nakedly cruelty enters our life! The man is still alive, but a doctor thinks in legal phrases. Disgusting, but man's death is the end only for him, life goes on and must be lived.

What a fool that Stepan Stepanovich is. Probably has been dreaming about a surgeon's career. They tell me that he has a fine imagination. How little do I know my kids. This is bad.

Steps.

A knock at the door.

"We are ready, Professor."

Am I ready? I must be. Everything is over, no more emotions. They have been pushed back into the farthest corners of consciousness.

4

MY TEAM

I AM DRESSING UP. Cleaning my glasses.

I am operating today in the small theater. It is especially geared for the AIK machine. Besides, it has a glass ceiling through which the operation can be observed. There are circular rows of seats there. It's a good thing that spectators are thus isolated, but it is unpleasant that the whole thing is so public. Surgery is not a circus.

I peek into the theater. He is already lying on his side covered with a sheet. No longer Sasha, but an abstract patient, or case, as we call them. I don't recognize anything familiar about him. I am not going to look at his face under the sheet, it is probably the face of a stranger.

Everything seems to be in order. The anesthetist, Dima, and his assistant, Lenya, are in their places. Lenya is rhythmically working the respirator bag. The blood falls from the drip and into the vein in infrequent drops. Peaceful blood. Maria Vasilievna is arranging the operation field. Now she is simply Masha or Marya, depending on the circumstances. We are very informal here. The assistant surgeons are standing by. The mechanics are sitting near their machine. All is peace and quiet. Only Marina, my theater nurse, is a little red in the face. Probably there have been slight altercations, she has a quick temper. Never mind, that's none of my business for the moment. Let them settle their own arguments.

Everything is so orderly and clean. The basins are still spotless. The only blood is in the glass drip suspended from an iron stand. Such a serene picture. If it could only stay like this to the end.

As always, I wash my hands silently and without thought, mechanically scrubbing with a brush. Everything has been thought out. Nothing new can be added. This is a special kind of calm which always comes to me just before the operation.

Finally I enter the theater. The incision has already been made and the breastbone split. The oozing blood vessels are being methodically closed by diathermic burns.

They put the robe on me, and the mask. I take my place beside Maria Vasilievna. There is not much room to work here, with four surgeons and the nurse, all crowding around one open chest.

"The valves?"

Just an affirmative nod. The words are unnecessary. I see them lying on Marina's table, three of them, of different sizes for proper fitting.

I cut through the muscles and open the pleural area. Of course! Surprises begin. The lung appears to be stuck fast to the chest-cavity wall. This irritates me; it takes time to separate connective tissues accurately, and our time is in short supply today. The patient's general condition warrants all possible speed. But there is nothing I can do but try to preserve my equanimity.

The pericardium is finally cut through. The heart comes into view. It shakes me momentarily. The X rays have shown that it was enlarged, but this! The left auricle is like a bag, the ventricle is enormous and pulsating strongly. When it contracts probably only half the blood is forced into the aorta, the rest flows back into the auricular area through a defective valve.

Revision: It means that the finger is inserted through the opening in the auricle and into the heart. I can feel the folds of the valve, they are rough and stiff and I feel large granules of lime. The strong flow of blood hits the fingertip at every contraction of the ventricle.

Actually all this has been expected.

For a moment I am thinking. Shall I just put in a new valve or try to mend the old one first? To put the artificial valve in is quicker, and the patient would not die on the table. At least he shouldn't. But then? Would the valve grow in? The heart is so badly deformed that the conditions for a successful ingrowth are not good. And how long would it serve in this case, even if it takes? Of course, if the plastic work proves to be impossible then the artificial valve will become necessary, but shouldn't I try plastic correction first? This would mean an extra hour for the heart-lung machine, which would bring on the danger of excess hemolysis, of liver and kidney complications. In Sasha's condition all these are very real dangers.

Like any surgeon I don't want my patient to die here, right now, on the table, or immediately afterward. That's the cardinal point. What happens later, weeks, months or years after today, would not be so acute.

But this is not right, not in this case. I must consider carefully and objectively, putting my own interests aside.

Again I insert my finger into the heart. For a split second a thought: How easy it has all become, a finger in the heart! I remember how I was bathed in sweat the first time I attempted it. Eight years ago I was younger. Today I would not start the career of a heart surgeon.

I am feeling, probing, considering. I should decide now, because when the heart is open it will no longer contract, and I won't be able to see the actual working of the valve.

I am not thinking about Sasha. I don't see his smile, don't hear his voice. I don't even feel that this is a living human being, all that has sunk into the subconscious. I am a craftsman examining a piece of material I have to work on. The conscious thoughts are all about the immediate problems, how best to tackle them.

The valve then. All right, we will postpone the final decision pending visual examination.

For a moment I glance at the glass ceiling. Over me, behind the glass, sit our doctors and nurses. Even some strangers. Just like a circus with gladiators. Death versus my little team. I needn't worry; this is a good team. They have met death before, and have beaten it many times. If only no one makes a mistake today.

"Let's connect."

This means connect the AIK machine. One tube is inserted into the right ventricle, it conducts the blood into the oxygenerator, the artificial lung. There it is collected by the pump, the artificial heart, and is sent through a second tube into the femoral artery. On the way it passes through a heat exchange apparatus which first cools the blood to produce hypothermia, and then, at the end of the operation, heats it back to normal.

The connection itself is a well-worked-out procedure, but it takes time. Everything is going on quite well. The tube is inserted into the heart without a drop of blood.

This is excellent. I know my job. But let's not count our goddam chickens. Shsh, Professor, no vulgarity! Sasha has probably never used such language in his life; his speech, like his thought, is elegant. I turn to the mechanics.

"Ready, girls?"

"Ready!"

"Let's go."

The motor starts up. It still makes a little noise, but nothing compared with the earlier models.

A quick checkup: venous pressure, oxygenerator, tubes, the pump action. The report: all systems are working normally.

"Start cooling."

I must now insert a tube into the left ventricle, to pump out blood seeping in from the aorta, and especially all the air that might get in there before the restart of the heart. This is something I overlooked with Shura: a bubble of air must have got into the blood and caused embolism, an arterial obstruction in the brain.

For a moment a scene appears before my mind's eye. A ward at night. The rhythmic movements of the artificial breathing apparatus. She is lying almost dead, cold and with no pulse. Only on the cardiograph monitoring screen there are infrequent electric jumps, showing rare and already unnecessary heart spasms. The brain has been destroyed by embolism, and the body is dying. All one has to do is to order the machine to be stopped, and in thirty seconds the heart would stop as well. Actually there is absolutely no point in continuing all this, but it is so difficult to say these two words: "Stop it." I shiver even now when I think about it.

This is what this tube in the ventricle means: it is

there to prevent the repetition of that scene. It must be inserted well. Actually this is not very difficult, we are forever doing it here. One must put in four sutures around the point of the insertion and then when the tube is taken out, the stitches simply tighten, and there is no hole.

All is done. Now we can take a little break.

We have about ten minutes before the patient's temperature is lowered to the necessary twenty-two degrees. We are all washing our hands with sublimate.

Marina is fumbling on her instrument table getting ready for the next and most important stage of the operation. The mechanics are taking samples for analysis. Dima is checking his battery of medications and ordering some additional ones. It's a pleasure to watch the team at work.

But actually we have nothing to do at the moment. A temporary lull before the battle. No thoughts at all in my head. I stand there and just look at the heart. I see that it is contracting slower and slower as the temperature falls. It is working now without any useful purpose, the blood circulation has been taken over by the machine.

"Marina, have you checked your needles and threads? Where are the valves?"

"Here, under the napkin."

"Show me one."

Here it is, the artificial heart valve. A little structure of noncorrosive wire to which some plastic material has been carefully sewn in such a way that there are folds just like those in the real valve. Not a bad piece of work done by Misha Savchenko. "The Moor," as one of the engineers has dubbed him. A good fellow, really, though not without some minor faults. The main thing, a thinker.

There is nothing else to do. We are waiting. Twenty-five degrees. The tissues are cold like those of a corpse, they are unpleasant to touch. The heart contracts forty times per minute. What we need is fibrillation, a spasmodic disorderly quivering of heart muscle which must replace the regular concentric contractions. Under these temperature conditions, this is tantamount to heart stoppage. It would give me an opportunity to work calmly and methodically without a time pressure; to cut, to sew.

Twenty-three degrees. Fibrillation.

"Here we go."

The auricle is cut wide open. A strong vacuum sucker clears the area of blood in a few seconds. Here it is, the valve, the holy of holies. Sanctum sanctorum of the human body. The key to its life. The heart is dry and motionless. Dead? No, not quite, there are still some hardly visible quivers. This is still life.

Everything is instantly confirmed. Our worst suspicions. The folds are shortened, stiff. Lime is deposited in large granules, and also in solid concentrations up to a centimeter in diameter. Along one of the folds, a wide crack. There it is, the "insufficiency." Corrective plastic surgery is out of the question, or rather, much too dangerous to even attempt.

"Removal."

I seize the folds with a clamp and cut the valve out at its circular base. This is a little frightening, I'm still not quite used to this. It reminds me of my first amputations: a leg is gone and it won't be there ever again. Instead of the valve there is now a formless opening. A new valve must be fitted in and sewed on along the edges of the hole.

Now starts the real torture. It is very difficult to put in sutures, there is no room to work. The damned needle holders don't hold needles firmly enough, they turn around like dervishes. It is impossible to calculate how much bile I have wasted cursing them, probably liters. Abroad they make special needle holders with holding surfaces treated with diamond dust. They hold a needle in a dead grip. I have seen them myself. But our ministry still will not budge. They don't give a damn. They don't have to work with them.

I am boiling with rage. If only one of those damned bureaucrats ever got on my table, I would show him a thing or two.

But somehow none of them ever gets here.

I am sewing for a long time, swearing all the while. I swear into the space, and at Marina who has misplaced the holder which I have specially selected for this operation, and at Maria Vasilievna who is not catching the ends of sutures fast enough. I swear at the whole goddam world. I confess, in my mind I use obscenity. In my younger days I used to move in the circles where such expressions were quite accepted. Then the war, of course. I had learned some choice bits there. The "maternity language," as one of my friends used to call it because of the frequent allusions to somebody's less-than-chaste "mother" in these oaths. Strong and colorful, but hardly a fit language for a distinguished professor. However, even if I had said it all aloud, no one would have paid any attention; they are used to my swearing.

But there is an end to everything. The valve is in its place, firmly anchored by thirty fairly good sutures.

Even, very good. I feel an enormous relief. I can at last look around and appraise the general picture.

"What is the hemolysis level?"

"It was twenty at the thirtieth minute."

"How long has the machine been working?"

"Fifty-five minutes."

"How is it you don't have a later analysis?"

"Their centrifuge does not work very well." ("They" are our biochemical laboratory.)

"Damn them! They never know how to handle their equipment, sons of bitches."

This is a totally unjust accusation, just a momentum of my irritation over the needle holders. Actually our laboratories work very well and perform a great deal of highly valuable precision work.

The hemolysis is still fairly low. All that is left to be done now is to stitch up the heart. Not too bad. Given good instruments, heart surgery need not be too troublesome. And patients needn't die. Undoubtedly in time we shall solve all our problems. We shall catch up and outstrip everybody, even the Americans. I'd better start working on a paper straightaway and then show the patient to the Society.

Whoa! What are you talking about? What paper, what Society? The patient is lying here with a wide-open heart, you have already scored one unnecessary fatality. And anyway, how can you think about anything like that at a moment like this?

I am ashamed of myself. There exists this little worm of vanity in everyone. You think you have smothered him with noble words and noble thoughts, but he is still very much alive. Could it be that it is this vanity worm who makes me tackle all these surgical impossibilities? I don't know. Sometimes I'm beginning to doubt myself. The most dangerous things to any man are fame and power.

Whatever it is, we are now sewing up the heart. This is also a delicate procedure, because the auricular walls are thin. We have started on the blood-warming process. The warm blood moves along the coronary vessels and the heart is becoming warm. Now it is very much alive, the quiverings are strong even though still disorderly. Technically this is known as large fibrillation.

When one is sewing up one needn't be in a hurry. There is no point in rushing. The warming-up process takes twenty to thirty minutes. In the operating theater all is quiet now. The only sound is the clattering of basins coming from the adjoining sterilization room, nurses are washing up there. There is nothing holy to them, they treat the operating theater as though it were a kitchen, little tramps. Fine girls, all of them.

The heart is now securely closed.

"The temperature?"

"Thirty-four. The rate of heating has slowed down a bit."

This is normal. The fibrillation is very energetic now; the heart is beating like a frightened bird trying to break out of a cage. One good electric kick would organize these disorderly quiverings into concentrated contractions.

"Get the defibrillator ready!"

This is an electric apparatus producing a shock of several thousand volts in a fraction of a second. It shocks the heart into resuming its normal rhythm, breaking off fibrillation. A very useful gadget.

And suddenly—oh joy!—the heart begins to work

rhythmically by itself. Something has happened, and out of chaos there has been born order.

"Normal rhythm!"

This is the voice of our Doctor Oxana, who is watching the electrocardiograph monitoring screen.

"You're late, Beautiful! We can see it ourselves!"

We are all overcome with joy. The defibrillator is a fine thing, but there have been instances when it failed to start up the heart. This has happened to us in the past. For hours we would take turns massaging the heart, squeezing it between our palms, pushing some of the blood through the lungs and body. Time and time again we would connect the defibrillator, but the heart would continue to fibrillate even though there was a smell of burnt flesh in the room coming from the electrodes. Then we would stop, exhausted, look at each other and say: "Death."

But this heart is working! What's more, it is working well! Fine, clean contractions. We must just warm it up with the machine for a while, and stop. Success! I am ready to scream with joy.

This lifeless cut-up body will again be Sasha, our dear clever Sasha!

"All right, kids. Let's extract the drainage tube from the ventricle."

Yes, it is about time. No danger of embolism. For the last twenty minutes not a single air bubble has slipped along the tube. We have been watching it like hawks. We won't be caught like idiots for the second time.

"Very well, Masha, my dear. You take out the tube and I'll tighten the circular suture. One, two, three—now!"

Just a routine, really. No point in dramatizing it. Suddenly:

"My God! Hold it! Vacuum sucker, you slobs, may the devil take you all! Get off your behinds!"

I still don't know exactly what has happened. Either the thread has snapped, or the muscle wall has broken through, but the moment the tube was extracted there appeared an open hole and, out of it, a spurt of blood a meter high! Of course, just for one contraction: the next second I close it with my finger. The crisis is momentarily over.

Now I must stitch up the hole. This is not at all easy, because the heart is pumping strongly and is quivering in my hand. Also the damned hole must be kept closed. It is difficult, but it is possible. This is not the first time, but somehow everything has gone so well that I didn't expect it today. Fortunately the machine is still working, so there is no danger of occlusion and death.

But this proves to be more difficult than I thought. Without releasing my finger from the hole I attempt to put on new sutures. But the moment I begin to tighten them, the muscle comes apart and there is a hole again. Damn it all! It is even larger than before, much larger! The blood spurts from it like a geyser. I press two fingers over it, but the blood continues to flow all around them.

Instantly peace and quiet have flown away. Everything becomes grim, dangerous, evil.

A calm winter day. A man is walking peacefully across the frozen river. Suddenly the ice breaks, he goes through and the black water is all round him. He fights, shouts in terror, grabs at the edges of the ice, but they keep breaking away under his fingers. The black water is overwhelming him.

It is the same here. Only the blood is bright red. A lot of it.

What to do? What to do?

"Patch! Marina, a plastic patch! Quicker, you cow! Get ready good strong sutures and a big needle! Sucker! Give me that sucker! Dammit, it doesn't work properly, you idiots! . . ."

Epithets.

I must put in a patch, like a patch which ships' carpenters put over a breach in a hull. But this is terribly difficult to do when the heart is pumping full blast and the damned needles are twirling in the holder like crazy ballerinas.

I don't know how long all this takes. First, a small patch. It doesn't hold, blood spurts from under it on all sides. Then, over that, another patch, a large one the size of a palm. Many sutures all round the edges. The blood is sucked off by a vacuum sucker and is sent back into the machine. The sucker can't cope with the volume of blood and some of it spills on my stomach and on the floor. For a moment I think about cooling the patient again and stopping the heart, but that would mean almost certain death.

Somehow, finally, I succeed. The flow of blood is arrested, just a few drops here and there keep squeezing from under the patch. A few more sutures, and the field is dry.

Yes, dry. The sucker is switched off. The heart is working evenly, though not as strongly as before; we haven't been able to replace fully the loss of blood. He is having a transfusion, and it is getting better.

I glance around. Everyone looks exhausted and unhappy. Miserable. No more elation, no more joy. They are still under the spell of the disaster, they are in slight shock, and they can't believe that this is all over. Correctly, too. Nothing is really over. We can now expect all sorts of mishaps.

A little superstitious thought: Perhaps this has been sent to me because of my treatment of Stepan? Perhaps I should have handled that affair differently? One can't insult people like that with impunity. But what could I do? I wasn't defending myself, but our clinic, our reputation, our patients. But still I could have handled it differently. With more humanity.

"Oxana, how are things with you?"

"Not very good, but tolerable. The myocardium appears to be weak."

Of course, it is weak. That's exactly why the sutures did not hold. Well, we must now wrap things up.

"How long has the machine been going?"

"A hundred and sixty minutes."

"That long? Hemolysis?"

"We haven't the last analysis, but just before the last complication it was eighty."

It means that now it is much higher. Pumping blood out of the wound and reprocessing it through the machine ruins erythrocytes, and we have repumped at least twenty liters.

"Stop the machine."

I look up. Behind the glass everyone is watching tensely. I become annoyed. Just like a circus, watching with bated breath, will he miss the net or not? Frightened and excited at the same time. But no, this is not true. Most of them have been honestly suffering this along with me. I must not think I'm an exception, an angel among villains. People are good. *Very good.* One must constantly repeat this to oneself. Otherwise life would not be worth living.

Dima is very busy with the patient. This is a difficult phase for him, the most responsible one. I deliver a corpse to him, and he must bring it back to life. He must restore proper breathing, he must regulate the function of the vessels and the heart. This is his department. He must quickly calculate everything, evaluate, make decisions. To match the heart action to the capacity of the circulatory system. To watch for a possible edema in the lungs as a result of weakening of the left ventricle. To build up the general tone of the system with hormones. To spur the heart action with special medications. To re-establish quickly coagulation of the blood, which has been reduced by heparin during the artificial circulation. One must know a great deal, and know how to apply this knowledge quickly and efficiently. Unfortunately in our work controls are limited. Electrocardiogram, the venous and arterial pressure, eye pupils, the color of the skin. Biochemical analysis, but each takes half an hour, at least.

The machine is working slower and slower. Then it stops altogether. We watch the heart intensely. Dima is constantly checking the pupils and trying to take the blood pressure at the same time. Finally he succeeds, and reports:

"Pressure, seventy. The pupils are contracted and constant."

This is the test for embolism. I am quite sure that there is no danger here. But then how can one be sure of anything in medicine, the most unsure of all sciences?

We are working with probabilities and approximations.

Through the hole in the auricle, closed by a clamp at the moment, I insert my finger to check on my new valve. It feels dry.

"No back flow of blood."

I measure the auricular pressure. Ten. It was thirty before.

"Let's pump a little blood into the artery."

The pump in the machine is turned manually several times. The blood pressure rises to eighty-five. This is sufficient for the moment. Now we can extract the tube from the heart, disconnecting it altogether from the machine. It seems to be working well.

So, actually, this is all. We must now put in a few sutures on the pericardium, insert a drainage tube into the pleural area and sew up the outer wound. But before this is done we must make absolutely sure that the flow of blood from the smallest vessels even has been fully arrested. The coagulation level is now low, and postoperative hemorrhaging is the most common and bothersome complication.

This takes almost an hour. Here one must not hurry. We are all slightly groggy after our tribulations, and only slowly coming back to our normal senses. But the heart *is* working well! Now, if he wakes up all right, we should be really happy. For the moment. Later on there might be other worries, other anguished hours, but up to now this operation has gone better than I expected.

We are putting the last stitches in the skin, when suddenly we hear the quiet voice of Dima:

"He has opened his eyes."

The way he says it one would think that nothing else could possibly have happened!

We knock our heads together leaning over Sasha's face. Yes, here he is, alive. His eyes are open. The look is still senseless, but a man with embolism does not open his eyes. One more burden rolls off my shoulders, off my soul. True, there is still a danger of bleeding or a kidney failure. The hemolysis after disconnecting the machine was a hundred and fifty. This is high. In olden days patients in such a condition died. But now we have learned to cope with it. If heart weakness does not develop, then the kidneys will evacuate this entire hemolysis out of the system with the urine in six to eight hours.

The second, or rather first danger is hemorrhaging. Unfortunately, it often occurs after operations with the prolonged use of the heart-lung machine. Some factors in the blood become damaged. This too will be corrected, I hope, in later models, but at this moment we must still contend with it.

"Dima, make sure that you have enough whole blood on hand, to avoid a night rush. You need at least two liters."

"I have already ordered it."

The operation is really over. The wound is taped up and they carefully turn Sasha over on his back. His eyes are closed again, but this is a normal postoperative sleep. If you pinch him he moves his arms and legs. No paralysis anywhere.

It has taken us five and a half hours from the moment of the first incision to the taping up. And if you count immediate preparations, over six hours.

"Professor, shall we start disassembling the machine?"

"No. Wrap the tubes up in sterilized napkins and

stand by. Marina, leave some sterilized material on your table."

"All this stuff has been exposed to contamination. I'll set up my table again."

"Good girl."

Very good. And so are all the members of my team. I'm proud of all of them.

All this is simple precaution. Everything should go well from now on. But one must be ready for anything. How many times in the past have I been forced to open the pleural area again to look for a single small bleeding vessel because blood kept appearing in the drainage tubes?

We leave the postoperative team in the theater and depart. People upstairs begin to disperse as well. The show is over.

We are blissfully relaxing now in the nurses' room. I collapse like a sack into an armchair and can't move a finger. Complete exhaustion, physical and nervous. How many both anguished and happy hours have I spent in this very chair! I yawn constantly. Oxygen hunger, as though I have been operated on myself.

As always, there are not enough chairs in the room and people are sitting on windowsills, on the table, even on pulled-out desk drawers. Our clinic personnel, who had been watching the operation from behind the glass, are all here, but no strangers; I don't permit them to disturb us after operations with their questions and comments. Here we are a family. We are all smoking. The windows are open. It is a beautiful May day outside, drawing toward evening.

How rewarding it is when the work is done and

everything has gone well! When you know that Sasha is lying there, alive. With a brand-new valve in his heart. With his life given back to him, and his letter in my pocket which I need not read now.

However, this is not only because it is Sasha, the man we all know and love. Had it been a perfect stranger we should have felt just the same. After successful surgery every patient is a joy. You have put your work into them, your soul. I don't know exactly how to describe this feeling, it is a special one, unlike any other.

"I never doubted you could handle that hole, Professor," comments Vasya.

We are all still under the spell of what we have gone through, and our conversation revolves around the operation.

"You didn't, but I did," I answer, blowing out the cigarette smoke. "For a moment I was quite lost. Of course, sooner or later we should have plugged it, the machine was still working and we could have pinched off the aorta. But the risk! As it was, the hemolysis figure jumped to a hundred and fifty."

"Still, I wasn't afraid."

"It's because you're young, Vasya, and cocky. You still don't appreciate the full scope of danger. I was the same way at your age."

"What happened, anyway? The thread must have broken. All four stitches couldn't have come apart at once."

This is Maria Vasilievna. She sits there exhausted, like myself unable to move. She is an excellent dedicated doctor, and a fine surgeon. My best, my closest assistant.

"I don't know really, Masha. All of a sudden the

thread was in my hand, and I threw it away. I had to plug that hole in a hurry. There was no time to look at anything."

Vasya is drinking water from a container in the corner. I am also very thirsty because my shirt and trousers are drenched with sweat. During some of these complicated operations I lose as much as two kilograms. I checked that once. But I don't care; at this moment I am swelling with happiness.

"Well, Comrades, we can put in valves, after all, can't we?"

"Yes, Professor, but the method of putting in sutures should be changed."

"Yes? How?"

Genya begins to explain. One must first run the sutures through the edges of the valve hole, without setting in the valve, and then run them through the edges of the valve itself. Only then should the valve be set in place and the sutures around it gradually and simply tied up one after another.

Very practical and clever. A very promising suggestion. I must investigate this thoroughly.

Now I must go up to my office and write the report of the operation. I hate it, and there is no avoiding it. It is a tedious task, but it is a part of a surgeon's work. And it is impossible to do it here, too much noise. Send them away? No, that wouldn't be right. These are precious moments for all of them, they are enjoying this relaxed communion, and they have deserved it. If they disperse now this quiet sense of great common happiness would be broken; each would find something to do. The wonderful atmosphere would be gone, and it would be impossible to recreate it.

"Genya, shall we go to my office and write up the operation?"

Genya is obviously unhappy about this suggestion; I can see it in his face. It is so peaceful here. It isn't often that the professor and the interns become so completely equal. But Genya must go. This is a question, but it is also an order, no matter how delicately it is given. I have selected Genya because of his excellent memory and his sense of detail.

He chucks away his cigarette, picks up the surgery journal and the case history. He is ready.

I also hate to leave, but I must. Besides, I have to change, I am wet right through. It is easy to catch cold, May or no May. I don't want to fall ill now. I want to do more operations like today's, to schedule a few of them as quickly as possible. All I need now is experience.

On my way up I look into the theater. All is quiet. The mess has been cleaned up. Sasha is asleep. Lenya is squeezing the oxygen bag. Dima is speaking softly to Oxana. I remember, someone has told me that those two are in love. Just gossip perhaps, but maybe true? Well, love has never hurt anyone, and people in love work well together. Fine kids, both of them. I need not worry, they should be happy together. Everything looks so tranquil, but this may be a misleading impression; who knows what processes are going on within that inert body? But by all outward appearances, all goes well.

In the dressing room things are piled pell-mell. Even my corner is not inviolate, somebody has dropped my undershirt on the floor. Never mind, I can pick it up. I'm too tired and too happy to be annoyed.

It is a relief to put on dry things. And it is pleasant to

look at Genya. So lean, graceful, muscular, young, as he stands there in his athletic briefs.

"Interested in any sport, Genya?"

"I was once, yes, but where would I get the time? I have different interests now. My study, my work."

"Well, work is work, but physical culture is important. Not competitive sport, that's nonsense, but physical culture."

This is one of my favorite subjects. I understood it when I turned forty and began to put on weight and my heart started to complain a little. I have lost every ounce of fat, and now I can engage in propaganda.

5

SASHA

My office. Well, it isn't so bad, after all. The walls are nicely painted. It is airy and light. The curtains are a bit old-fashioned, dark, heavy, with little knots all over them. I ought to change them for something bright and modern. But then, what for? With the years I'm losing my taste for possessions. Perhaps I'll understand Diogenes when I grow really old. A barrel would do fine, provided there is a bathtub in it.

"Sit down, Genya. Let's start."

We are writing laboriously, I in the journal, and he in the case-history folder. We are trying to remember all the smallest details. The operation is still new, it must be described meticulously. Later on, the surgery reports will grow shorter and shorter, until there will be nothing to say but "normal" and "usual."

It is interesting to consider one's thought process; it works on several levels at the same time. Here is one plane: thoughts about the operation. On another, thoughts about Sasha, medicine in general, surgery, blood circulation, artificial heart valves. In between come all sorts of nonsensical trivia, some immediate impressions absorbed by eye and ear. The curtains again, the broken fountain pen on the desk, the picture of Lenochka in a frame. A sort of subcurrent of thinking.

I feel peculiar now. Excitement, clarity, freedom

from all anguish. This differs strikingly from the pre-operation jitters. Then I was crushed by the anticipation of danger. There was a single thought chain, the operation and everything connected with it. Also excitement, but of a completely different kind, tense and unpleasant. Fear, an unhappy realization that this is now unavoidable, and that I must go through with it. Nervous concentration. But now everything is clear, interesting, sharp, vibrating. All surgeons, I suppose, treasure moments like these.

Finally the report is finished.

Genya is leaving.

"Tell them to call me in if necessary."

"Nothing will happen, Professor. The operation was wonderful." (I also think so.)

It is six-thirty. A whole hour after the operation. I'll wait for a couple of hours more, then go home. All will be well, of course, but still I'd better wait a little. It is best not to make plans and be ready for anything. Hemorrhage, kidney trouble, edema. Anything. Some surgeons make appointments half an hour after operations. That I don't understand.

I light a cigarette. "I'm trading bread for drags of stale tobacco . . ." There is a soldier's song that goes like that.

I wish I could listen to some music. I should get a tape recorder like those they have now in all the "best houses." There are professors who work only with tape recorders. Nonsense. My dictating is too limited. Music? Also impractical. How many minutes like this come my way, combining both free time and happiness?

Has anyone spoken to Raya? I don't want to do it. Maria is friendly with her; she has probably already told her everything. I was too abrupt with Raya this morning.

What shall I do now? Read some dull dissertation? I'm sick of them. The life of a scientist is full of papers. First you write them, then you read them, correct, criticize, listen to them during meetings.

It is funny: I am a *scientist*. Deep inside I can't accept it. I am a doctor, a physician.

Shall I go down again and chat with my boys and girls? Somehow this doesn't work so well nowadays. I realize with sadness that I'm becoming more and more separated from them. My age? Or perhaps, as some say, my new sense of self-importance? No, that can't be true, because honestly I know that there is no reason to feel that way. I am a good doctor, but many of those boys and girls will be better than I. This is the main thought, a sort of mental close-up. But in the background there stirs another one: *Nonetheless I am I. I have accomplished many things which others couldn't do. My latest victory, the valve. I have written reams of scientific papers, published several books. If one counted up my dissertations alone. . . .*

Stop, Professor! Just let vanity get out of hand, and it puffs up like a toad. A scientist indeed! Don't fool yourself, your so-called works are not worth the printer's ink used in them. In a few years no one will even read them, they will become so hopelessly outdated. No one can stop the progress of surgery. We operated on stomachs first, then esophagi, then lungs. My papers and books on abdominal surgery are forgotten today; the same will happen to my works on heart surgery. But again there is an egotistical little thought: Still, I have been a part of this progress. Yes, of course, but have I really originated anything? And if I have, has it changed the world? Do I want to change the world? Yes. Everybody wants to. Everyone wants to eliminate war, to make all mankind fine and decent.

Only science can accomplish this. Science in the broad sense of the word, starting with atomic fusion and ending with the education of children. Adults, too.

Sasha, for instance, is a true scientist. (How wonderful it is that he is alive! Medicine has really come in handy here, I shouldn't knock it.) I have learned a good deal from Sasha. My own work has become more meaningful to me. I have started to see the skeleton of science, the bone structure of thought. Sasha says that true science starts only when it is possible to begin counting and that it was Mendeleyev who first said that.

Should I read Sasha's notebook? I think I have some right to do so, now. The letter, no. It is too private, too personal, but the notebook must contain some impersonal scientific thoughts. Mathematics, probably. Too bad I don't understand it. Whenever I come to a mathematical formula I feel a slight nausea; I quickly pass it over or just abandon the book.

My curiosity begins to be slowly aroused. Shall I just thumb through it?

But supposing they overlook something there in the theater? What time is it? Just ten minutes since Genya left. I can stay here. Those youngsters are very alert, very clever. And I am so tired I can hardly move at all. Old age. It would be so good to have a cup of tea now. Too bad I haven't organized that department for our evening vigils. Now I must forget about this. Another cigarette. "I'm trading bread . . ."

A rather thick notebook. The title covers the entire

first page. "Random thoughts." Pretty flat. A title for a grammar-school composition. But no, let's not judge too severely. Everyone is entitled to a mistake. Haven't I done many stupid things in my life? And some even not altogether honest? Some? Even?

I am leafing through it. A strange notebook. Among the scientific passages there are personal entries, a sort of confidential notes. Obviously this is not written for publication.

"It is sad to realize that death is so near. All that would be left behind me would be some models, molds, clichés. My articles, this notebook. Letters which are never wholly sincere, some impressions in the minds of others, some photos in albums, but all this is static, frozen, lifeless. It would be nice to leave even one simple working model at least . . ."

I remember some of our conversations. My contention: why leave anything? All this is vanity, an illusion of immortality. But Sasha had another theory. Man as a biological system disappears, but if one considers a higher system, humanity, something can be left.

This, of course, is true. Humanity is not merely a collection of human beings; it includes the fruits of their activities, the molds of their thought: things they create, books, pictures, machines, buildings. The man dies but the models created by him continue to live their own lives, independent from the man who created them, and in some instances, begin to live only after his death. Sometimes they are beneficial to humanity, but they may also be harmful. Mostly because all such models (Sasha's favorite word) are lifeless, they cannot adapt themselves to changing conditions, they can't be influenced or argued with, or improved; they lack dynamism, lack life. Now I am beginning to understand Sasha's idea of creating a working model of the human brain which could live and undergo evolutionary changes, grow, improve and create in its own turn.

The dualism of human nature is terrifying. On one hand, an animal, just like a wolf or monkey. On the other, an integral part of society, a higher system governed by a set of ethics.

Very well! At least now we have something. The overall mathematical interpretation of the world, the universe. Philosophy and mathematics. The question of eternity. I think Einstein claimed that there is no eternity as such, everything that can be measured must have an end. I don't quite understand all this, and I won't even pretend that I do.

The chapter: "Connective elements, systems and subsystems." This I understand; he explained it to me during our talks. The human organism, for instance, is a system composed of subsystems, the organs. The organs are also composed of subsystems, the working components. Those in turn are composed of their own subsystems, the molecules. The molecules have their own subsystems, some known to us, some as yet undiscovered, and so on, ad infinitum. Going up, we have collective, society, humanity, the systems in which man is a subsystem, and all these systems are connected and correlated among themselves on the basis of physical laws of mutual dependence and compensation, the exchange of energies and physical particles.

And people? They communicate with one another by words and symbols. This is also physical, but this is physics of a more complex type. Here is the explanation, a chapter titled "Information." We are accustomed to the conventional sense of this word, "giving out data." But this is how Sasha treats it: "changes in physical influences in time and space, taken outside its physical carrier and expressed by various physical means." Something rather obscure. "In correlation between advanced systems we deal not only with direct physical influences, but with influences modified in time and space and accumulated in the form of models or molds, i.e., in changes created in structures. An example. One man says something to another. The spoken words are physical air waves. But for some reason they don't affect a fly, or even a cat. This is because man has a capacity of extracting information from these particular air waves, the meaning of words. To achieve this he receives the air waves which are then translated into nerve impulses. They travel to the brain and are registered there in the cerebral matter in the form of thought molds, or models, composed of nerve cells. To create sense these models must have a certain successive order, the element of time, which is one of the elements of information. The same effect is achieved by visual symbols transmitted by our eye, symbols or letters, and here we are dealing with still another element, space."

Now I am beginning to understand the meaning of the term "model" as used by Sasha. For instance, in the above examples words are models, composed of letters or sounds, but they are understood by the recipient only if they fit the ready models existing in his brain. If someone were to speak Chinese to me I could not extract any information out of that type of air wave any more than a fly or a cat!

"Information is impossible without modeling." Just as I said above! "A model always represents some sort of structure, reflecting a system, or its modification in time and space. A house built of wooden blocks is a model of the system of a real house. Words written on paper are models, reflecting the relative order of sounds of human speech. A drawing of a machine is a model. Musical notes are models. Mathematics deals with sets of models. When we see a picture a cerebral model is created in our brain, composed of connecting nerve cells. Models can be primitive or precise. A child's dawing of a house is a primitive model, an architect's, a more precise one."

Interesting perhaps, but too complicated. Information, models. What for? People used to live without them. Physics, chemistry, materialism. All this does not appear to be enough now. I've heard all this from Sasha many times; I understood some of it, but not all. Somehow this sort of abstract science fails to excite me.

A new chapter: "Learning."

"Learning is a process of producing models. The brain is a powerful model-producing installation. What is 'learning'? It is getting to know the structure of something, its system, its relation to other systems, its changes in time. All this information is stored in the brain in the form of thought symbols composed of nerve cells. Those are models. Sometimes we know something well, a more or less precise model. Sometimes only superficially, a primitive model. But we never know anything absolutely, because no model is ever a perfect copy of the original, especially a model composed of nerve cells which in themselves are subject to changes and influences."

Very well. So the brain is a model-producing machine, a computer. A purely mechanical arrangement using electric impulses to produce action. All this is not easy to accept for a man brought up with the recognition of qualitative differences between living and dead things. But then what does the word "understand" really mean? "To get accustomed to and learn to use something," a definition of some celebrated physicist. I don't know how to use some of Sasha's theories, and therefore I don't understand them. And I don't want to accept anything without understanding, solely on blind faith.

"The limits of learning. No model-producing installation has an unlimited productive capacity. Also it cannot create models of any systems more complex than itself. At best it can reproduce the main structural elements of the original, perhaps generally defining its main functions. The more developed the model-producing installation, the more precise are the models it can create. If one uses only one thousand wooden blocks one cannot create a model of a large city, but with a million such cubes the resulting model will be more accurate.

"The speed of learning, information digestion and assimilation, i.e., model producing, is also limited. The total model-producing capacity of the brain is equally limited. So is the brain storage space. It is fortunate that the human brain has a faculty of forgetting, i.e., clearing room in the brain for new information."

Ah, here is something that might be important to a doctor:

"An average human brain contains fourteen billion cells. The whole human body, over three hundred billion. Therefore the human organism as a whole is a much more complex system than the brain. If we take into consideration the fact that each cell is composed of billions of various molecules, the complexity of the human system is enormous. Can we expect then that the brain model of the human body will ever be precise? No. At best we can expect only very primitive general images. We cannot even expect the brain to model accurately any of the systems composing the human body, or to define its main functions. Neither would such partial modeling be very useful. Unfortunately, the human body is a system in which not only does the behavior of the whole depend on the function of the components, but vice versa, the function of the components depends on the function of the whole system. Therefore, in order to understand, create a model of, the human body the analytical study of the components is not sufficient. It is necessary to create a more or less precise working model of the human organism as a whole in which one can observe and study each component, or a number of components, or the whole system, as the case may be."

This is sad, but true. No one human being, no matter how brilliant, can understand and know the entire human body and all its functions, and since there is a complete interdependence of all component parts, without understanding the whole one cannot understand fully the function of component parts, or organs and systems composing the human organism, and vice versa. Up until recently medical science held that it was sufficient for one specialist to concentrate on one function of the body, another on another, et cetera, and then for an overall specialist to combine all this knowledge and treat people. This is clearly impossible, because there is no such superdoctor who can absorb and evaluate all such information and use it properly, and therefore we are working with approximations and generalities. And if sometimes we are successful it is only because the human body is a self-regulating structure which compensates for all our ignorance and many of our mistakes. It would be indeed wonderful to create a mechanical superdoctor which could combine the brains of all specialists. And this is exactly what Sasha is aiming at.

Do you see what clever things I know? Cybernetics. Yes, I have learned to respect it deeply. "The science of the correlation of living organisms with mechanical systems." All our medicine is an attempt to regulate living systems by mechanical and chemical means. The problem is that it is far from being precise. It can't be precise, because there are no precise models; and there are no precise models because our model-producing mechanisms are not sufficiently developed to produce them. Also, the brain is far too slow. That is why we always make mistakes: our brain is not quick enough to absorb and digest the great volume of information thrown at it in the course of even a simple surgical operation. This has become especially apparent since we started to operate on the open heart, disconnecting it from the system. Here the self-corrective faculty of the system is interfered with, and we are left more or less on our own. And we often can't cope with the amount of information which we must absorb, evaluate, digest and act upon with split-second precision. Hence, the mistakes. We make them even when we know basically what must be done and, given the necessary time, could do it.

Probably the same thing happens to everyone attempting to operate any very complex mechanism whose action once started cannot be arrested. I suppose the pilot of a passenger airplane feels this way when confronted with some mechanical malfunction while flying over terrain excluding the possibility of an emergency landing.

The "limit of knowledge" theory is an interesting one. One must think deeply to understand it. I know, for instance, that my own brain is definitely limited. I can construct only a very simple model of a complex system, but a simple one is fully within my mental grasp. The thousand wooden blocks. One can build a rather good model of a barn with them, but to build the Moscow University skyscraper? At best it would be a very approximate likeness.

The limitation of the speed of learning is easy to understand. The process of memorizing goes on with a certain velocity, a totally insufficient one. And that is the extent of brain capacity in time. I read on:

"Human learning is collective. We are learning about the world almost entirely from ready models created either in the past or by our contemporaries. This greatly extends our brain's modeling capacity, but not indefinitely. A limited collective, just like an individual, cannot fully absorb the entire amount of information necessary to understand a very complex system, because there is no effective way to combine many brains to create a single gigantic modeling installation, a colossal superbrain."

I can see the logic of this thinking from my own experience. Dozens of physicians, precise specialists in their respective fields, examine a patient with their mechanical aids. They produce hundreds of analysis sheets and charts. But another man, some tremendously clever doctor, must evaluate, absorb, combine all this material to understand the workings of this particular human system, and to act with sufficient speed when time is limited to minutes as, for instance, during open-heart surgery. But the trouble is that there is no such superdoctor. Specialists are extremely helpful in that they furnish us with their fairly precise models, but to combine all this information into a single working model is the task which I, for instance, cannot perform. My own modeling installation is not sufficiently developed for that. Therefore much of this precise information remains unused, or else I digest and absorb it too slowly for practical application.

I know what Sasha is leading up to, his answer to the problem: a mechanical brain. Here it is! "Even collective learning cannot fully assimilate and retain all the information inherent in a complex structural system, and therefore cannot handle the problems of using and governing it. But now science offers us an opportunity of creating artificial working models of theoretically unlimited complexities. Scientists can deposit all their knowledge into such a mechanical brain, as a writer puts his thoughts into a book. But there is an important difference: a book is dead and static, while an electronic brain can live, develop and create out of the elements deposited into it. For instance, various specialists would be able to deposit all their knowledge of various functions of the human body into the machine and let it function as a whole. In time a precise working model of the human system can be created mechanically, ready to operate, or live. All that one would have to do would be to switch on the current and the model would come to life. Then a precise model of a morbid germ could be introduced into it and the machine would become sick, and the whole complex of subsystems, organs and cells, would react to counteract this invasion. This would be a true working model of the human body, so complex that no single human brain, or collection of brains, would be able to even imagine all its capabilities. In this way, human genius would take the first step towards dynamic accumulation of information on an unlimited scale. This, in my opinion, is the most staggering development in the entire history of humanity."

I have heard all this before from Sasha, about this mechanical accumulation of knowledge. At first I was skeptical. But then, if one compares the volume of knowledge in ancient Greece, for instance, and today, the gap is gigantic. This has been achieved by the gradual accumulation of knowledge in the collective human brain, already a very primitive form of storage battery, but this accumulation process has been acquired by absurdly insufficient means compared with the capabilities of electronic accumulation of the same knowledge. The amount of thought material lost in the process has been appalling. Still the amount of this accumulated knowledge is growing all the time and urgently requires more advanced means for digesting and storing it, and using it. With the old system of recording knowledge in books, very imperfect models, no single human brain could absorb and apply this information wholly and usefully; some details could be absorbed, but never the whole picture. To a doctor this limitation is very well known; it would be a blessing indeed to have a working model of the human body, for instance, where all the problems could be solved by simply pushing a button and getting a precise answer. Only then could we hope to be able to treat people without mistakes.

Also books are dead, they do not develop. All medical works of fifty years ago are ridiculous to us today while the working model would be living and developing constantly. At least that is what Sasha promises.

Perhaps one day this will be possible. The first electronic computers, still very primitive models, are already solving instantly the most complex mathematical problems out of reach of any single human brain. They will become more and more complex, more and more precise, and through them, man—no, humanity—will master the foremost secrets of nature and life, and learn to work with them. According to Sasha, there is absolutely no limit to the mechanical capabilities of such superbrains endowed with the capacity of not merely working with the information fed into them, but producing their own information.

A devilishly exciting idea! If an artificial heart valve can be built, why not a brain? I am too old to participate personally in this work. I don't know mathematics, my profession squeezes everything out of me, it taxes my brain beyond its capacity. But I'm looking with hope and admiration at people like Sasha who will fulfill, or at least advance this work. Of course Sasha may be overoptimistic in his estimations, but then science seems to develop with ever-increasing tempo, more has been achieved in the last twenty-five years than during the last three centuries, and if the process continues at this speed, there is practically no limit to what can be achieved.

Exciting, yes. At the same time one feels a sense of frustration watching this process. Here man stands before a tremendous river of knowledge rushing at him, and all he can do is to take a miserable little gulp. When

I was young I thought I could cope with everything coming my way, that there were no limits to what I could learn. Now this self-assurance seems simply stupid.

How are things going in the operating theater? Have they taken him into the ward yet? Of course not. It has been only half an hour since I left. Shall I go there, or read a little more? After all, Dima has a pretty good modeling installation on his shoulders, and I would only be in his way. Somehow the presence of a senior colleague often inhibits one's activities.

And so I read on. Here Sasha goes into a rather complicated theory of programs. The precise codes of behavior allegedly developed in the brain, which rules all our actions through nerve impulses. Simple programs, complicated programs. According to Sasha, they are being formed all the time and then activated under certain conditions to produce the dynamic process called life. They are all interrelated, one program producing and activating another, all in accordance with precise physical and mathematical laws.

Programs, programs. He has spoken to me at length about them. Everyone knows this word. There is a program of a concert, for instance: the successive order in which the participating artists appear. The conductor holds a piece of paper, the model, in accordance with which he conducts the concert. There are programs for economic development, programs of political parties, et cetera. But Sasha treats this term differently.

This is how he explains it: "According to each program one element of the system acts upon another, passing on the necessary information, whereupon a certain action of a series of actions is produced in accordance with the model of the program."

Generally, Sasha's style in this chapter is not too good. There is a tiresome repetition of the same awkward terms. According to Sasha, all these programs are developed and stored in the human brain. Some of them are simple, some complex, some brief, some lasting, such as for instance a program for a surgical operation. The model of each of such programs is composed of precisely prearranged actions, each causing and activating the next. There are variations in such programs, a choice of several variants, but basically they are all there and activated in a certain precise manner.

He wrote this probably after listening to my description of operations—I told him once that there is little actual thought in the surgeon's brain during surgery, that your hands react to the developing situation almost automatically. I said it more or less as a joke (though basically this is true), but to Sasha this is no laughing matter. He is dead serious about his programs.

Still it is hard for me to believe that all our actions are governed by programs physiologically forming in our brain, and that there is nothing more exciting and spontaneous behind them.

A picture: A violent argument during a meeting of the Surgical Society. I have called a certain professor a stupid ass and run out of the room, slamming the door. I sit now in the dressing room near the window, smoking, deeply ashamed of my conduct. Were all these actions deposited in my nerve cells? Was my stupid outburst just an activation of one of my programs? Of course, there are fourteen billion cells in my brain and mathematicians can create absolutely endless combinations out of them with more zeros than the human brain can imagine, but still—

Another picture: I am sixteen. My native city. A park in Solenyi Gorodok. (Meaning Salty Suburb. Why *salty?*) An evening. A bench under some chestnut trees. I am sitting with Valentina, reciting a poem of Esenin to her. (We were all overwhelmed by Esenin then.) In my mind I repeat: Valentina. Valya. Valechka. Valushenika. Darling. My palms are wet with emotion. I don't want to touch her or kiss her. I'm filled with emotions which can be described only by an old-fashioned word, *exalted*. I am ready to perform any prodigy for her. I am praying for an opportunity. Was that also a program? No, I can't believe it.

All right, to hell with it, let it be a program. If there are fourteen billion cells, it makes little difference whether this is God or a conscious freedom of will. The terrifying thought is that they threaten to reproduce all these things mechanically. I can imagine! A computer in love!

There is something about this in Sasha's notebook. "The program of human behavior." I suppose he attempts here, with the help of cybernetics, to give mathematical answers to the unanswerable questions What is man? and How can one know oneself?

I am turning the pages. This chapter is too long, too verbose. I really must go downstairs and see how everything is going. Suddenly the name of Sigmund Freud catches my eye.

I remember our talks. Freud, Freudianism. Sasha is violently opposed to these theories. He is enraged because we haven't produced anything to rival them. As I remember, his arguments ran something like this:

"Freud is a psychiatrist. He works with morbid material, diseased human mind, and based on his experience he attempts to create a system covering the entire human behavior. If one accepts Freud, one must forget communism once and for all. Therefore, if we want to build an ideal society, we must create a new psychology without which any planning of any new society is impossible. Conscience is governed by life, but this also works the other way around. As the cultural and economic prosperity of people grows, the close correlation between life and idealism grows as well. One cannot throw one of them aside. And this is exactly the growth stage through which we are passing now."

All right, let's see. "The program of human behavior."

"Man is a complex self-regulating, self-adjusting, self-educating, self-correcting system." Self, self, self. For a while I am confused by this ever-repeating prefix. I suppose what he means is that this particular system is so complex that it can produce its own programs. Self-education means that it collects experiences and adjusts itself to them. Self-correction means that it is capable, in conjunction with other factors, of changing even its basic structure. This we in medicine know very well. And so on.

"All actions of man just as of any other system are carried out in accordance with certain programs; in other words, they are governed by the organic function at each given moment. The programs change as certain portions of them become fulfilled, or under the influence of outside factors, which is true of any self-correcting mechanism such as, for instance, a simple compass. However, all such changes are limited to the structural limitations of each system, in other words, each system acts only within its program. Physically there is no basic difference between man and some very complex machine. In both, the complexity of structure governs the complexity of behavior programs. This premise should not frighten us by its seemingly crude mechanical approach. We must bear in mind that there is no limit of complexity which can be developed in any mechanical arrangement."

No, this is something I can't accept. No machine can be as sensitive as a human being.

Now Sasha attacks so-called freedom of will. According to him, this is a misnomer; all behavior is governed by purely physical impulses and elements. He admits, however, that the human being has two sets of programs, animal and human. The first set has an organic connection with the animal origin of man; the second is produced by the society in which he lives. Society is the only factor which makes man human. Without it, man would remain an animal, like children brought up by wolves and monkeys.

The animal programs are instincts which are innate in human structure. They are powerful, often overwhelming. The human programs are acquired, but they are equally powerful, often keeping all animal programs in submission. Instincts are found in all living forms, but even some animals living with man develop some human qualities which make them act contrary to their instinct interests. There are known cases of dogs consciously sacrificing their lives for their masters in utter defiance of the self-preservation instinct, the most powerful one of them all.

There is nothing particularly new in all this. But the thought of animals is close to me. Our lesser cousins. They love, they hate, and more important, they suffer.

And they are brutally abused. Man is cruel. Hunters, for instance. I can understand the destruction of predators. But what about birds and squirrels?

Sentimentality. What can we expect from animals when we haven't learned to be human to each other? However, I am sure that in the future many of the inhuman facets of life will be corrected. Chemistry will provide steaks.

I suddenly remember a true story about animal fidelity which I heard some time ago.

Siberia. The taiga, virgin forest wilderness. A trapper found a wolf cub and brought him up. They spent most of their time together in a forest cabin. When they went to the village, the young wolf would stay close to his master. The trapper probably loved him very much.

1941. The trapper is drafted into the army. A sad parting with his pet. The trapper leaves the wolf with his old taiga hunter friend.

Three years of war and suffering. The trapper returns, crippled. His family had disintegrated. The old man tells him the the wolf had refused food and finally escaped back into the taiga. The trapper is sad, but what can he do? He returns to his forest cabin, finds the window broken in and a wolf skeleton in the corner.

In his next chapter Sasha deals with ethics, which he also explains on a physiological basis. A rather imaginative approach again firmly based on the program theory. Physiology of imagination, inspiration, talent. According to Sasha all this can eventually be built into machines, and they would then write poetry and compose music. Even create philosophical theories.

"Freud maintains that base influences, dictated by instincts, always overcome social ethics. This may be true in psychiatric experience, but not in life. Man differs from animal by his capacity to develop human programs in his brain so powerful that they can crush instincts. History and daily life provide many examples of that. This gives humanity hope of the eventual creation of the future perfect society, communism.

"However, one must not feel complacent. Social programs can overcome animal instincts, but this is not an automatic or easy process. When instincts are highly aroused they may temporarily sweep aside all moral principles ingrained in man by education. It is necessary to remember that men differ greatly from one another on the level of their moral development. Therefore, we arrive at an important premise: society must not only ensure correct social education, but also create conditions which are not conducive to overstimulation of base instincts."

Yes, with this I agree. The elimination of hunger is not enough to achieve universal happiness. There must be justice, a set of workable laws governing marriage, divorce, education, housing conditions, child welfare, all human relationships, but also one more condition, the minimum limitation of the reflex of freedom.

All this Sasha has preached to me. The thought is clear. It is not necessary to repeat the instances and examples which he cites in this chapter; they are self-evident.

But to build such a perfect society is not an easy task. The mechanics involved here are extremely complex and the modeling capacity of even a collective brain is sorely limited. That is where we need all Sasha's wonder-working machines.

It is the same thing with medicine. Without complicated machines the proper work in this field is impossible, and even with machines it would have been extremely difficult without the self-correcting and self-regulating faculties of the human body. And, of course, without the most accurate controls. I remember the lecture of one academician: no proper planning in any sphere of modern life is possible without electronic computers.

Another thought: Instincts and their suppression. Hunger, for instance. The association: Leningrad during the siege. Love of one's country. Masses of people suppressed hunger for it. Unto death. Eight hundred thousand people died of hunger in Leningrad during the three years of the siege.

And the contrary example: For lust, for greed, people violate every moral law. Criminals. One often reads about them in newspapers, and wonders, Why?

And what about myself? No. I have weaknesses. I am no paragon of virtue, but certainly no criminal.

I must go.

It is almost seven o'clock.

I will smoke another cigarette and go. Is there anything there to read further? No, just literature. Suppositions, theories. I'll read all this later. A chapter about the conscious and the unconscious. The physiology of thinking processes, creating models, the activating of some, temporary suppression of others and relegating them into an active reserve of the mind. All this is fairly well known. And here, another line of arguments against Freudian theories.

I am no specialist on Freud, but I think his main theory has defects. Much too much stress is placed upon the sex instinct in its darkest and most obnoxious forms.

There is no denying it is powerful, but surely not powerful enough to dominate life in all its forms, in arts, science, politics.

Stop it! This is not your sphere.

But then, why not? This is medicine. In the Freudian teaching about the unconscious there are many logical premises. I think Sasha has borrowed a few things from Freud. He denies it, however. He claims that he works on the plane of pure information. I can't judge. I can't quite understand this plane. Until recently in our country they did not recognize any instincts or any unconscious. They claimed that man could be molded into any desired form. All people could be turned into angels very quickly.

This is a question open to argument. Sasha claims that it can be solved scientifically on the basis of pure mathematics.

Nonetheless, paradoxically, the so-called medical intuition has been always recognized and accepted. A doctor looks at a patient and comes up with a precise diagnosis. This is nonsense. Without knowledge no diagnosis is possible. Perhaps with very experienced practitioners the necessary information is stored in their brains and then comes out suddenly as though by a miracle. I don't know. This has never happened to me. I would prefer to have a good diagnostic machine that works like a computer.

I turn over the pages. I see that further on Sasha attempts to deal with passions, extreme interests, fixations, tries to find a physical law for them. "False ideas can seize upon the human brain just as strongly as true ones."

Yes, the possessed. Have they been responsible for

culture? Passionate scientists, revolutionary heroes, eccentric inventors? The cracked ones, as our kids call them. It seems so to me, but I may be mistaken. Normal people want more money, they build, construct, create; this too is progress. Greed and vanity are instincts, but they often stimulate cultural achievements. And passion is a human quality. A beautiful quality.

But how it can lead one astray! One can become passionately involved in an absolutely worthless idea. There have been many examples of passionate but misguided people. Fanatics. Therefore, an intellectual check is important. Or at least a well-developed set of moral controls.

It seems that I too begin to preach cybernetics and rationalism. Some specialist!

And still true enthusiasm is a great thing.

Another chapter: "Subjectivity."

"The impression of the universe and selection of one's behavior in it are often distorted not only by the limitation of one's learning mechanism, but by the function of one's own reaction sphere."

Here follows a long explanation. It appears that every time information is fed into one's brain it is compared with molds already existing there, and the selection of a fitting mold is often influenced by one's own preference for one of them. This often leads to the distortion of one's logical behavior. At least this is how I understand it. There are many cumbersome technical terms in this chapter. "And so the limitations, faulty selection and subjective preferences often make the human behavior of an individual unexpected, unreasonable and illogical."

Well, one must accept this. When such behavior is

based on ignorance or stubbornness one must have patience to understand and explain. With most normal people this is usually possible.

Ah, here's a really interesting chapter! "Happiness." This I must read. "A dream of happiness—"

Suddenly I stop dead.

There are running footsteps approaching. My heart sinks into my stomach.

The door flies open.

Someone in white stops in the doorway.

"His heart's stopped!"

"Good God!"

I leap up and rush out. I actually run, taking several steps at a jump, risking a fall and a broken hip. And in my head there are snatches of thought:

"This is it, the end. But why? What for?"

6

DIMA, LENYA, OXANA, MARIA VASILIEVNA

THE PROSTRATE BODY OF SASHA. A corpse? Dima is standing on a stool sharply pressing Sasha's chest: a closed-chest heart massage. Lenya is furiously squeezing the oxygen bag. Oxana is wringing her hands. The nurses are fumbling around, not really knowing what to do. Pale faces, frightened eyes. A picture of utter despair.

"Adrenalin! Have you tried adrenalin?"

"Not yet. We started the massage—"

"Marina! Two cubic millimeters! Quick!"

I want to massage the heart myself. Perhaps I can do that better—experience. Quiet, you fool! Dima is doing it very well, he is younger and stronger.

"Oxana, what do you see on the screen?"

"Nothing, because of the massage—"

No, nothing can be done. Nothing. How could I, how could I? How could I sit up there, reading? A scientist!

"Dima, stop for a second! All right. Oxana, what do we have there?"

Silence. Tension. Oxana is watching the screen. It seems that all this takes an eternity.

Oxana sighs loudly.

"There are some irregular contractions."

"Dima! Massage! Adrenalin!"

Keep going, keep going, Dima. Perhaps we shall succeed. Good God.

The adhesive tape has already been removed from the wound.

"Just a second, Dima. Stand by."

A long needle, direct into the heart. One cube of adrenalin.

"Massage!"

One minute. Two. Silence.

It is dark in my soul. Despair. What for, what for? No, I shouldn't lament. There is no law of retribution here. Everything is clear. We are fools. Bungling idiots. Limited modeling installations. We need machines. But this does not help me now. I'm not a machine. I'm alive.

But what about Sasha? All right, let's see.

"Dima, stop massaging! Oxana, watch the screen! Somebody, take his pulse! Hey you, stop pumping the bag! Don't you know better?"

"Good contractions, about a hundred per minute."

"Even pulse."

However, all this information is superfluous. I can see the chest working. The heart has picked up, and picked up well.

"Pupils?"

"Contracted. They contracted immediately after the start of the massage."

There is a collective sigh of momentary relief. Faces have become relaxed, eyes quiet. But within me everything is trembling, and at the same time a strange sort of weakness is spreading all over my body. I feel that I may collapse.

"Give me a chair. And you—get down. Why are you standing there like an idiot?"

This to Dima. He is still standing on the stool, erect, tall, angular. A handsome boy, really.

Once again Sasha has gone away from me. All I see is an unconscious body. A stranger. And I myself am absolutely empty inside. I know what may happen now, and therefore I'm not at all happy.

"Now tell me everything. Oxana, don't take your eyes off that screen."

"There's not much to tell. Everything was going on fine. Here's the record. He opened his eyes, several times. His breathing was improving normally. We were quite satisfied. Oxana disconnected her screen for a moment, wanted to move the apparatus, and suddenly something stabbed me in the heart. I raised his eyelids—wide pupils! I shouted like mad and started the massage. Everyone came running."

I should have been here sooner! Several times I wanted to, but couldn't lift my behind from a chair.

I am studying the records. When I left, the pulse was a hundred and twenty. Then gradually it had started to fall off, and the last record, eighty-five. This was twenty minutes ago, about ten minutes before the stoppage.

Dull anger, annoyance. I hate to look at all of them, I hate even to swear. Mistakes, mistakes again!

"What have you been doing here? Didn't you see that the pulse was falling off faster than normal? That meant that the vagus [the wandering nerve] was acting up. You were probably in a hurry to go home? I know that it's late, and you're tired, but the patient doesn't care. And you! Relaxed after your success? Thought that you were heroes, and everything was over? Probably sat here wagging your tongues."

Silence. Everyone looks hurt.

I'm not being just. For that matter, we had all relaxed. And I sat there thinking about lofty matters, reading those idiotic theories. Sasha didn't know to whom he was giving his notebook. Had I been here I wouldn't have missed it. Am I sure? No.

We should administer a little atropine to lower the irritation of the pneumogastric nerve, the so-called vagus. That's what I think, but perhaps the situation is more complicated than that. A devilishly complex machine the human being, and we are helpless facing it. Much more could have been done, engineeringwise, to help us; all our mechanical aids are still too primitive. All right, let's think about that later.

I must learn to treat my co-workers with more consideration. They are probably thinking now: "To hell with this damned clinic. You work like a slave, put all your soul into it, and all you get is criticism and reproach." I must learn to control my temper, and my tongue. One tone softer:

"How long do you think the heart was stopped?"

Dima jumps in eagerly:

"I don't know exactly, but it couldn't be more than a minute or so. Oxana just disconnected her machine."

Lenya cuts in:

"The pupils contracted immediately after Dima started the massage."

"All right, take all tests. Blood for an analysis. Oxana, how is it going?"

Oxana's eyes are glued to the screen. She is terribly upset. Red in the face. She knows that she should not have disconnected the monitor, even for a moment.

"Not bad. Not any worse than before. A hundred and forty."

"That's the adrenalin. It will wear off."

It takes two–three minutes for all calculations. The report: everything is satisfactory.

But all this does not cheer me up. Of course, it is good that he is alive. So far. But first of all I don't know how long the heart hadn't been working. I don't particularly trust their reports. Not that they are lying, but it is difficult to evaluate everything properly. Then there is a natural tendency to imagine that the situation is better than it really is. We all need this for ourselves.

If the heart stops for over five minutes the cortex dies. And who wants Sasha without his brain, or even with a damaged brain? However, this is academic; cases like that always die. I've never known one survive. Yes, this is all very sad.

The second point. Very few patients survive the post-operative heart stoppage. Usually it is possible to start it up, but not for long. It stops again, the second time, the third. Then forever. But the valve has been inserted well, the stoppage was of a reflexive kind, and not because of any organic weakness of the heart muscle. There is hope. Not much, but still—

"He opened his eyes!"

Everyone is satisfied, but there is no real elation. The danger is still too great. Only Dima is openly beaming. Perhaps it was he who made the original mistake, but now everyone can see that this mistake has been corrected. Almost. And that he indeed noticed it in time.

We must develop control machines so that we do not have to depend on people's attention. What attention could Dima give when he has been in a state of extreme tension for seven hours?

Once again death is in the room. I am well aware of

this. There is not too much hope. However, the heart is working well, I can see Sasha's chest heaving. I don't know, but we must hope for the best. This is the effect of adrenalin, of course. And what will happen when it wears off?

What shall I do then? Go home, lie on my couch, drink a glass or two, cry a little with dry eyes, and then, operate again? For how long?

But what else can I do? Retire? I know very well I wouldn't be happy away from my work. I should consider myself a coward, a deserter. I'm not suffering from inflated ego, but how can I abandon all this, all these people who regard me with such respect and hope? I can't offer them anything except surgery. I'm not a youngster, and my brain is not that adaptable. I'm no Sasha. And Sasha won't be there any longer . . .

Funny. All these people, all those books have inserted into me those programs of public service, and they have gone deep into my soul, have become my instincts. I can't get away from them. I believe Sasha, who says that everything is mechanical; but not to me. To me it's pain, anguish, tears.

I am not a hero. I fear pain, for instance. I'm not afraid of death, no, but I'm afraid of pain. This is true. Death holds no terror for me. Just a pose? No. This is true. Freud was probably not a very big man if he considered instincts to be unconquerable.

Enough of Freud, enough of theories. Because of them I sat in my room longer than necessary. But Sasha is alive! I must now try to keep him alive. To save his life, no matter what.

I am going through the whole thing in my mind. Just like a machine, but probably not as well. The agitation of the pneumogastric nerve has already been curbed by adrenalin. Now we must build up the normal heart contractions. There are ways of doing that.

"Let's administer some AFT and Lanacordal. After that, a complete checkup."

The girls start to move. They are doing everything quickly, precisely. It is a pleasure to watch them work. Yes, they work well, but they didn't figure things out soon enough. Am I sure I could have done so? No, not sure. But still my modeling installation is perhaps better. Thank you.

Now all we can do is wait. Oxana is watching her screen without batting an eye. Dima and Lenya take the blood pressure every five minutes. They have connected the suction system to the drainage tube from the pleural area; there was no hemorrhaging before, but now anything can happen, the heart and the pectoral area were squashed quite a bit during the massage. Some damage is practically unavoidable. Even the sutures could have come apart, especially in those patches. The pump starts and immediately some hundred and fifty cubes of blood flow into the ampoule, and then it starts to drip in large steady drops. This is much too much.

"Transfusion. Keep the cube-per-cube balance!"

Problem, and a serious one. What if the hemorrhaging doesn't stop? Open the chest and check on all sutures? This is always dangerous, but after a heart stoppage, extremely so. Now we shouldn't even think about it. The stoppage may recur at any moment. We must use our entire arsenal of antihemorrhage medications.

"Come on, children!"

I rattle off the Latin names of the drugs. There is a new spurt of general activity.

I am sitting brokenhearted, filled with dull anguish.

No one leaves. There are about ten doctors here. It's long past seven o'clock, and they serve no dinners here for overtime workers.

"Open the windows, the air is foul. And why are you all standing here? Some of you can go home."

Silence.

There is a great deal being written about communism. Some claim that it is practically here. But, in fact, there are plenty of skeptics. "What communism? So-and-so was caught stealing, so-and-so is using protection and pull." I personally don't think any perfect society can be built so quickly, but when I look at my young doctors I feel warmth coming into my heart. Many of them are married, have children. They would probably like to go to a movie or play with their kids. But instead they stay here until seven, until nine in the evening, the whole night if necessary, getting no overtime bonuses or free-time benefits. And they are here on time the next morning with red-rimmed eyes and never a grumble. Of course, now and then they miss something, make a mistake. "Bunglers! Idiots!" Like Stepan this morning. I wonder if he's gone home? No, I saw him sitting in the ward. He used to play chess with Sasha. I am sorry for him, but what could I do? That boy undoubtedly died because of his negligence, and Onipko is still on the danger list.

Yes, about communism. I have been to America, visited their hospitals. Physicians there are working hard, from morning till night, and I think, have compassion for their patients. Just like us. But no, not quite.

I'll never forget a scene I saw once, through the glass, just like our glass. It was a very difficult operation with artificial blood circulation, very complicated, very troublesome. The patient was still in the room, barely alive. And in the corner the surgeons and anesthetists had gathered for a conference, speaking in low voices and writing something on a piece of paper. I asked the interpreter, a very nice fellow, what they were doing. The microphone was still connected, and he listened through his receiver. "They are dividing the fee for the operation."

I felt sick. I didn't want to look at them any longer. I told the interpreter, I couldn't contain myself, but he was surprised. "But didn't they earn this money honestly?" What could I answer? Would this be possible with us? No. These forty years have not been spent in vain. True, the result could have been better, and we must do our best to improve it all the time. There are still too many egotists, too many deviations. So many that sometimes I feel frightened. Is it possible that these green sprouts will wilt?

No, this is my depression talking. They will not wilt.

"Well, Oxana?"

"A hundred and twenty-five, but growing weaker."

Now Dima comes in:

"The pressure is falling off, too. It was a hundred and ten, and now only ninety-five."

Oh God, here it comes! The inevitable. The pressure will keep slacking off, and then the heart will stop again. "Don't stop, don't stop, I beg you!"

There is no one to beg. You can rely only on yourself. And on those kids there.

Dima again:

"Perhaps we can add adrenalin to the drip? To keep up the pressure?"

"Yes, add, but only very little."

Adrenalin makes the vessels contract. This builds up the pressure, but also puts an extra stress on the heart. It would have been better to build up the contractions. But we have administered all the available medicaments for it, and they haven't helped. No, I'm still afraid of adrenalin.

"Dima, you haven't done it yet? Don't. Let's try cortisone instead. A large dose. Have you tried it?"

The report: not yet. How could we have forgotten about it? We don't know yet exactly how it works, but in some cases it performs miracles. Apparently it builds up the function of all cells. Very good stuff.

Liuba, the anesthetist nurse, fills a syringe and inserts it into the drip. Now it will enter Sasha's body along with the blood.

Meanwhile the bleeding continues. True, it has fallen off to forty drops per minute, but this may be the result of the lowering blood pressure.

"Send a request for some additional blood. Two liters. Fresh."

How much blood have we used today? Probably about three liters. But this is a special case. In America they order five liters for a routine operation. Why should they economize? The patients pay, the unemployed sell blood. I had seen those advertisements in their newspapers: "Blood donors wanted, immediate payment." And I saw them queuing up outside the blood banks, mostly poorly dressed people, some of them drunk.

What time is it? It is half an hour since the stoppage.

This is not bad. I must telephone home and tell them I shall be delayed indefinitely and not to wait for me. My wife is probably worrying about Sasha, he is her favorite, too. She always sets him up as an example to me, such courtesy, such good manners. This is true, but manners are not the main thing. Very well, I will go.

I get up.

No, I'm afraid to leave. Frightened. It seems to me that the moment I go his heart will stop again. I'd better wait here until the heart pressure becomes stabilized. Are you sure it will? No, of course not. I usually prepare myself for the worst.

Everyone is silent. Dima is taking the pulse. Lenya is working the bag. The patient is asleep. We don't want to wake him up.

"Pressure?"

"Ninety to ninety-five."

"Oxana?"

"No change. A hundred and twenty."

I must sit and wait. Surgery is not merely operations, excitement, passions. It is also waiting, sweating, suffering. "What to do next?"

There is nothing to do at the moment. Unless the bleeding stops I shall have to open the wound. Oh no! I feel cold shivers running down my spine. I'd rather die than hold that heart again in my hands. Dramatics. But almost true.

Life and death. How much there is in those two simple words. Poets, scientists. But in fact, all this is very simple. At least this is what Sasha used to say. I remember his words. "Living systems differ from the dead only by their complexity. Only by their program of digesting information." Our living things on this earth are composed of albumen bodies. Out of this there are various structures operating on different levels of complexity of their programs. Microbes derive nitrogen from the air. The worm reacts to the most primitive influences and his behavior is limited to a few basic movements. This is the limit of his program. Man is capable of absorbing and retaining a great deal from outward influences, or information, as Sasha calls it. His movements are extremely varied. But still he is a mere machine operating in accordance with a very complex set of programs. Once this would have sounded like sacrilege. Because then people only knew how to produce the most primitive models, they accepted things and did not attempt to compete with nature. Now all this has changed, or rather is changing, more and more. Man will build some incredibly complicated electronic machines which will model life. They will move, feel, think. They will compose music and write poetry. Why can't that be called life? It is not important from what material a complicated system is constructed, albumen molecules or semiconductive elements. Houses are built of different materials, but serve the same purpose. The important point is to make an artificial structure which could absorb and digest complex information, and act upon it with certain correct programs.

Then man can become immortal. Not a whole man, but his intellect, and probably even his emotions.

I am handling the subject as a hard-bitten cybernetist. Too bad no one can listen to my mental models. Then they would know what wide interests I have. Everyone considers himself intelligent, and I'm no exception. But am I, in fact? I have remembered Sasha's words all right, but I'm not at all sure that all this is so.

Too many elements must be used to create the human organism. And who would arrange all these elements in the correct order? Still, there are machines even now which no single man can design and build, and they work.

Memories again. I remember one night Sasha was daydreaming in my study. I don't remember his exact words, but I can reconstruct the sense:

"An electronic brain will be built, a tremendous one. Mathematicians and engineers have not the slightest doubt about it. This will be done, and perhaps sooner than we think. A machine which will be capable of development and learning, and infinitely faster than any man. They would, for instance, connect it to a scientist. The machine would instantly absorb his way of thinking, all his knowledge, his character, his feelings. It would become his alter ego. The scientist will die, but his mechanical brain will continue to live and create."

"Deliver lectures, write treatises, listen to music, swear at its assistants?"

"Don't laugh, Professor. When it grows old, because machines also grow old, it will pass everything on to its mechanical successor."

And so, eternal succession.

But then he contradicted himself:

"No, unfortunately, all this will be much more difficult. No system can be fully repeated. It is impossible to create an exact electronic copy of *my* brain, with all its cells and peculiar combination of cells. It is possible to create another one, better than mine. It would take everything from me, like a son or a good pupil, but it would remain a thing apart. It would develop and perfect itself, leaving me far behind, and drawing further and further away from me. Then I shall die. But something will be left of me. Perhaps even a good deal. And this is pleasant to contemplate."

"An old father expiring in the electronic arms of his genius son?"

Sasha just smiled dreamily, and his eyes sparkled.

I am sitting with Maria Vasilievna in a corner of the operating theater. While I was reading upstairs she had been making the rounds of the wards, but as soon as she heard about the stoppage, she came in. We are both thinking our own thoughts, but they are the same. About him.

"Masha, have you any hope?"

Her look is serious and sober.

"Yes. We must save him. It's our duty."

"As if anyone cared for our duty!"

"I just can't imagine him dead."

"Neither can I, but there's so little we can do."

I turn to our kids: "How is he doing? Any improvement?"

Dima:

"So far the pressure's holding up. Pulse, a hundred and ten. We still have no analyses."

"Send for them. Hurry them up."

"It's no use, they are doing all they can. Valya is doing everything herself."

Valya is our laboratory head. She is one of my friends. We have many people working in the clinic, some of them are just my collaborators, some are friends. I don't particularly fraternize with them, don't hold any special conversations, but I know that they are my friends.

Maria Vasilievna is the closest one. She is not looking

very well. I wish she would dye her hair at least. This is how age creeps up. She came into the clinic a mere slip of a girl. Well, there's nothing to be surprised about. That was twenty years ago. Yes, twenty. Twenty years of living together, working together, growing old together.

"I have gone through the wards. Nothing particular to report. Let's call off the operation with the AIK machine for tomorrow. I, for one, have no strength left."

"All right, Masha. Call it off."

She continues:

"Everyone is jittery, wondering about Sasha. They are whispering in all the corners. Raissa Sergeyevna fairly jumped at me. 'He is already dead, but you're keeping it from me!' You should have spoken more kindly to her this morning. She is a good woman—"

"To hell with her! I was kind enough. The fool!"

This is true, this is the way I feel. Here he is, and he can die at any moment, and I'm heartbroken, but I don't regret my decision to operate. Had I refused, as his wife begged me to, he would have started to die in two–three months in the ward and it would have been too late to do anything then. And I would have seen a constant reproach in his eyes. Even if we are defeated, it's better to go down struggling. Better for me. And as for him, much better.

I could have refused, of course, on purely medical grounds. No one would have reproached me. I could have been lying on my sofa now, reading. There is a new novel by Steinbeck. Lenochka would have been chirping around me. Idyl. But in the depth of my mind, a thought: Coward.

And in the morning, his look: "You have let me

down, you bastard." And all I could have done would be to lower my eyes, and avoid his room.

No, it's better this way. I'm trying to be severe with myself. Am I absolutely sure that my decision was right? Well, not one hundred per cent, no. We could have waited a little, could have experimented on a few lighter cases. Could have gathered experience. We could have avoided the heart stoppage, perhaps, and the hemorrhage. But what about the liver? Would it have lasted long enough? How do I know? Perhaps. Once again I come up against the same thing, no precise knowledge. Cybernetics could have helped here. To hell with cybernetics! I'm sick of the word.

Petro approaches.

"I have given Onipko a fluoroscopic examination and changed the drainage tubes. His condition is still critical, but I'm pretty sure he'll pull through. Stepan is with him."

Stepan is with him! Trying to expiate his sins. He has a short memory, this Stepan.

I know that Petro is trying to extract a reprieve for Stepan from me, taking advantage of my weakened state. Not yet. I limit myself to a noncommittal statement:

"All right. We'll see."

I could not say no outright, I am afraid to tempt fate. Superstitions. I will go into this tomorrow. And today, am I trying to fool God? Funny. Man is funny. Today God could have squeezed out of me any condition in exchange for Sasha's life. Outside this, his chances with me are not good. Because I really don't need anything—neither money nor fame, not even love. I just want peace, to be left alone, if possible. But there is no God to bargain with.

Time is passing. Fifty minutes after the stoppage. The heart action seems to have stabilized. The blood pressure remains constant, eighty to ninety. He woke up, became restless and was given sedatives. Now he sleeps like a baby. Only his lips remain blue, the heart does not pump enough blood. But all the analyses are satisfactory.

Our hopes are rising. There have been cases when patients survived even late heart stoppages. True, not many; perhaps one out of ten. However Sasha's odds are already much better. Usually after having stopped, the heart works for five . . . ten . . . fifteen minutes, then stops again. All the really dangerous time barriers have been passed. He still has a chance. And so have I.

Miracles in medicine are rare, but nonetheless they happen.

One night a few years ago I performed an emergency operation on a lad with a mitral stenosis. He developed edema. This is like an avalanche, a man can die in thirty minutes choking on blood foam accumulating in the lungs due to the high pressure in the pericardium, caused either by a heart condition or emotion. The boy was scared by something—if I remember correctly, by the death of a man in his ward. They brought him into the operating theater blue and unconscious. I could only wash my hands in alcohol, and Marina had barely enough time to throw a sterilized sheet on the table. In a few minutes I separated the folds of the mitral valve with my finger, the pressure came down, and the young man came to life. I went into the next room quite satisfied and started to write the surgery report. And suddenly, just like today: "The heart has stopped!" They noticed it at once, on the electrocardiograph monitor screen. We gave the boy closed-chest massage, a success. The blood pressure went up to normal. I went back to finish my report. Another stoppage. We started the heart up once more. In twenty minutes, again. After that I went home, unhappy, after the third stoppage there was no longer any hope. So I left my kids to take care of it. When I returned to the clinic the next morning I didn't even bother to ask, I was so sure that the man was dead; but suddenly they told me that he was alive! After I left, the heart stopped again, and again they started it up with massage. It worked for an hour and they decided that all danger was over. They moved the young man into the ward, and there, already in bed, his heart stopped, for the fifth time! They started it up, this time with final success. The man is still alive. This is a miracle.

I wish there were more of them.

However I must telephone home. Now I can leave without too much risk, Maria Vasilievna can take over for me. Also they are not likely to grow negligent again, they are still too scared. But still, just in case:

"Look, children, don't go to sleep. I'll be up in my room for a while. You, Oxana, especially. If you have to leave even for a moment, ask one of the doctors to take over. I don't want that screen to be left unattended even for five seconds. Clear?"

Affirmative nods. I leave.

My office. It is almost dark. I don't switch on the light, it is better like this. Quieter. I telephone home:

"Hello? Are you all home already? How is Lenochka?"

My wife answers. All is well. Lenochka wants to know

how soon I shall come home. She has grown up. She no longer asks, "Is everything all right, Daddy? The patient died?"

How do I know when I shall be back. I give a short report, feeling sorry for myself.

"I won't be home yet, unless he dies. Don't worry about me. No, I haven't eaten. I'll eat later. It is not important."

My wife is not particularly distressed about my fast. She understands that it is ridiculous to speak about food at a time like this. In fact, I even have some. On my table I see a glass dish of fruit salad and a sweet roll. This has probably been brought in by the night head nurse. But where did she get such a roll? It is not from our kitchen. Some anonymous donor, someone has brought it from home to nibble at night. Perhaps Valya from the laboratory?

First, a smoke. "I'm trading bread for drags of stale tobacco." The melody has stuck in my head.

This is medicine for you. Once the heart had originally started, it had absolutely no reason to stop. Obviously we had overlooked something, had not appreciated fully the real situation. Everything could have been controlled in time by simple medications.

Doctors laugh when I talk to them about cybernetics. But this is not a laughing matter. Only machines can solve some of our problems, remove the uncertain human element from our work. So far we have only abstract ideas about it, nothing that can be applied immediately. But this depends on all of us. It will take a great deal of time, study, effort and money, to dress these abstract skeleton ideas into mechanical flesh, but it must be done. A machine giving us exact information on the state of the patient, a computer with a colossal memory, and then other machines designed to treat each case properly, surgically and chemically.

I won't live long enough. Besides I'm not very well suited for this work. Not clever enough, and not sufficiently educated.

But how useful all this would have been in Sasha's case! He is still young. If we can keep him alive for a few more hours, everything will be fine. At least, for today.

Through the opaque door I can see a vague silhouette. Someone has come to the door, stopped there and is listening. This annoys me. It is not someone from the theater, they wouldn't have waited.

"All right, who is it? Come in! Why are you standing there like that?"

". . . Why are you standing there like that?"—the words of the old woman from Pushkin's "The Queen of Spades." Association. The machine continues to work. My favorite opera.

The old nanny from the reception room shuffles in.

"Excuse me, Professor. Some girl, or young lady, wants to see you. I didn't want to bother you, I know you don't want to see anyone, but she insists."

So she is thinking about me, this old woman, takes pity on me. But this doesn't help me. I'm all alone, and no one can help with my burden.

"What does she want?"

"She says it's personal."

"I've got nothing peronal to discuss with anyone."

"Yes, but she sort of looks personal."

Oh yes, of course! How could I not have guessed at once? Certainly this could not be a woman looking for a love adventure, even though surgeons often have a strange attraction for women, rather like famous artists. This must be *that* one, the one to whom Sasha wrote his letter. A wife is in one part of the building, and a mistress in another. But no, how crude of me! What sort of mistress can she be to Sasha, now? I'm thinking this way only because I'm unhappy. Well, I suppose I must speak to her, for Sasha's sake.

"All right, let her in."

I am switching on the light.

I don't want this conversation. Almost as little as I want a conversation with Raya. But this is my duty, my moral obligation. I must discharge my obligations. I owe a lot to people, they have been responsible for my being what I am today. No, they have not given me anything! No? And what about those children who had been brought up in the jungle among animals? They had remained animals, and I have developed into a human being. "The programs of behavior are developed through education." This is from Sasha's notebook. One should never exaggerate one's own importance.

It will be interesting to see the woman with whom Sasha is involved. I must listen to her and try to be polite.

But what shall I talk to her about? She would not be able to understand anything. I have no kind words to offer anyone at the moment. I need them myself.

Sasha said, "Read the letter, then you will understand." No, I can't read it now. I don't feel easy about Sasha any longer. I can't forgive myself that hemorrhage and that heart stoppage.

Let her come. I can give her nothing but a brief

factual report and a few polite words. Even for Sasha's sake. If I can't help Sasha, what can I do for her?

There she is now, behind the door. It didn't take her long to climb the stairs. Or probably the old woman had brought her up before coming to see me. Thinking that I would not receive her, she could always take her down. "What's the use of running up and down?" Logical.

A knock at the door.

"Come in!"

The door opens. She enters.

I look. Yes, quite good-looking. About thirty. Good figure, fine legs. Ridiculous, *legs,* at a moment like this! An old reflex. Stupid impressions, completely out of place here.

"Good evening. I've come to inquire about Sasha, Alexander Popovsky."

"Please sit down."

A pause. She is very good-looking.

"Please forgive me."

The beginning of the inevitable phrase, ". . . for disturbing you at this hour when you must be very tired." And so on. But no, she falls silent.

The next inevitable program: "What can I do for you?" But I hold it back. Let her talk instead. I have no feeling whatsoever toward her.

"Tell me, will he live?"

No, it is impossible to avoid those trite questions! Just impossible. I feel anger stirring in the back of my mind.

"I don't know. We are doing everything in our power. Forgive me, but I don't feel like explaining anything to you at the moment. If I am brief you won't understand anything. And I have no time for lectures.

Besides, I don't even know who you are. The only close relative of Popovsky I know of is his wife."

Stop! She jumps up, becomes red in the face. Dammit, how crude can I be?

"Then excuse me. I didn't know you were like that."

I am so ashamed of myself I feel like dropping through the floor. I can see that she has some sharp words ready for me. I wish she would spit them out. One should be slapped in the face for behaving as I have. I must try to repair some of the damage.

"Unfortunately, I'm not an angel. Don't think all this is easy for me, I am very tired, very upset. If you can, don't feel offended. We will talk about this later. Just be patient and don't ask silly questions. Here is a key, it opens the door of the next room. It is my private laboratory, and there's a couch there. Go inside, lock yourself in and don't switch on the light. I will speak to you when I'm ready. Is that all right?"

"Yes."

She takes the key and leaves without even looking at me. How unpleasant! Perhaps my last words have smoothed it over a little? I can imagine Sasha looking at me with reproach in his eyes. God will not forgive me for this. But he must be understanding. Yes, but also very stern. One can't hurt the weak and the unhappy, even when they ask stupid questions. Retribution. What nonsense crawls into my head tonight. Ridiculous. There is nothing, everything is just a machine.

The problem is that no one knows how to run it.

. . . and Night

7

IRINA

Again I am alone in my room.

Shall I go down to the theater? There are people there, activity. My comrades. They understand everything. Well, not everything, but a good deal.

Well, apparently I must read that letter. This is not curiosity, there is no room for that now. But if she's here and I must speak to her eventually, I must know how to do it. Perhaps he is planning to marry her if he gets well? Or break off with her altogether? I should really know.

I bring out the envelope, open it. A neatly written letter; the handwriting does not betray any excitement. But then I am no specialist on graphology.

Now, let's see.

My dear little Irina! My darling!

It is so difficult to write a letter which may become the last one. The operation is booked for the day after tomorrow. True, I'm afraid that the professor might refuse at the last moment, but this is improbable. I have convinced him there is no other way out for me.

Today I'm arranging my affairs; writing to you, sorting out my papers. I will leave all this with the professor. I am certain that you will come to see him.

But remember that even in sorrow a person must behave with dignity.

I wanted so much to write you a tender and beautiful letter, but somehow this doesn't work out.

Tomorrow will be too late to write. I'll have visitors in the daytime, and in the evening they will stuff me full of medication and will not permit me to do anything. Do you know how fear accumulates within one as the end draws near?

I am trying to order myself not to succumb to it, to hold myself in check. I'm trying to think about science, about Serezha, about you, but fear continues to grow in the back of my mind, and now and then it comes out with an innocent little thought like this: "If you'd only give yourself a couple more weeks, you could have worked out the program of imitation reflexes." The devil is so clever! He does not work directly, he does not tell you: "Refuse!" No, he acts craftily, insidiously, from your subconscious.

I struggle. I resist him all the time. I am a mathematician. I know there are no two weeks any longer, any day my condition may become inoperable.

And still there is fear. Sometimes various images appear. Thunderstorms, hurricanes, scenes of sharp discussion, or you, as it all used to be when there was strength, excitement, keenness of emotion. And then my heart begins to ache: Irochka, my little Irina! And I begin to lament miserably in my soul: "Why me? Why has it happened to me? What for?"

I am probably expressing all this badly. I've never liked long letters, but today I see no end to this one. You must forgive me. I have become weak, I want to talk my fill before death. I don't deceive myself. Only before my doctors and my wife I try to put on a brave front: let them think that I am full of the "will to live." Doctors say that this helps a patient. Unfortunately my morale is quite low. I insist on this operation simply because I can't act against the most elementary logic: with the operation I have a small chance; without it, none. Therefore I'm trying to hold myself together, and not go to pieces, not to invoke the program of grief.

Then I'm sustained in my determination by fatigue. I'm tired of being sick, I'm tired of living like an invalid, and I have become disillusioned in many things. The only thing really left is science, my work. To think, to search for connections between elements gives me pleasure. I am willing to foreswear everything else for it. Please don't think that I exaggerate my importance; I'm no Newton, and I don't think I'd ever greatly benefit humanity. (But in the back of my mind, a question: Perhaps I can benefit humanity in some degree, after all?) Even if this happened, it wouldn't be important to me, I shall be dead before my work could ever be brought to conclusion. If people should be able to use it later, to build on my premises, it would be beneficial for the higher system, society, and not for me. Therefore I have no vanity. But the very process of thinking, creating, finding new things is incredibly exciting. Because of it I'm willing to face all risks. Of course, maybe I'm not altogether sincere in that; in my subconscious there stirs another thought: If I get well I'll be able to have some animal programs as well. But those programs have never been very important to me.

Forgive me for all this twaddle. My brain is in a turmoil.

Remember how we used to study the mechanics of happiness? I have calculated the balance of my potential happiness. Without the operation, it is nil, and no matter what should happen, it will be an improvement. That is why surgery is necessary even though the risk is very high, probably about seventy per cent against me.

Now let's suppose that I survive. I shall never be completely well; without doubt the functions of many organs have been badly undermined and will never return to normal. Asthma will probably remain and all my physical programs will be curtailed. I shall have to diet because of my liver. My rheumatism will periodically become acute; it means that I shall always have to keep out of drafts and close all the windows. In a few years the artificial valve will start acting up, this probability amounts to about forty per cent. [How I wish I had such mathematical optimism! Let's continue.] *Then again, decompensation, and so on and so forth. Therefore, when I consider everything, my enthusiasm is not very great. Sometimes I think that the best way out for all of us would be for me not to wake up after the operation. Oddly enough, this thought also gives me some comfort.*

No, of course, I want to live; I want to model the human psyche. I am deeply involved in this work, poisoned by it, and nothing is very important to me compared to this. My animal programs are inhibited by my illness, and I don't know whether I want to revive them at all. At the moment they seem utterly unimportant. Even my son, Serezha, has become dis-

tant. All I have is some naked ideas which are breeding in my brain day and night. I understand everything, including the mechanics of my involvement in this. I am guilty before you, but what can I do if I can't feel otherwise? Pretend? Lie? It seems to be too late for that. The fact is that science programs have taken complete possession of my brain, a true hypertrophy. This may sound a ridiculous phrase to you, but these terms are dear to me because I have invented them.

All this is sad, my darling. Perhaps it is cruel to tell you all this, but to whom else can I talk? You must forgive me. You are alive and you are well. You are not a romantic girl of Turgenyev's and not an Anna Karenina. Concentrate on your own programs, and please don't leave too much room there for myself. You know how unpleasant it is to be a bankrupt debtor.

This is all, my darling. One must end the letter sometime.

Just in case—goodbye!

I kiss you tenderly, like then.

SASHA.

The letter has been read.

Let us have a smoke.

A strange impression, a slightly unpleasant one, I expected romanticism, passion, but instead, just programs, mathematics. He has asked me to pass this letter on in any event, whether he survives or not. He should have written two letters: a tender one in the event of death, and this if he remains alive. He refuses her love, this is quite clear. And he does not love her. But why must she know it if he is dead? What practical purpose would such knowledge have? Has he ever loved her? And is he capable of real love, as others love, with all their souls? His heart belongs to science. "Hypertrophy of dominating models." He has spoken to me about them, explaining the mechanics of passion, of fixation. Yes, normal animal programs have been dying in him for some long time now. This is normal; during decompensation many bodily functions become inhibited. But is love, true love, a bodily function? Apparently it is, with Sasha.

Not a pleasant letter. Somehow, not very noble. I did not expect this from Sasha. But then, why not? I remember some of his statements. Ideals are unnecessary. Sasha is very intelligent, but his emotional make-up may be only average, the thing which we call soul. He doesn't want to see her any longer. He sacrifices her to his fantasies. Or perhaps he is tired of lying? Perhaps he has made a resolution: If I get well I will not deceive anyone any more. In everybody's subconscious there are some dark corners. Storage room for dishonesty.

However, I must not jump to conclusions. I have not sufficient material to pass any judgment.

I would like to read the chapters in his notebook about love and happiness. No, later. I've already been caught this way. I'd better go down and see how he is doing.

Why didn't she come to see him before the operation? Probably he had asked her not to. And how would I have acted in his place?

I am walking down the stairs anticipating surprises. For instance: I come into the theater and find everything in perfect order. Sasha is awake, the heart works well, the hemorrhage has stopped. They are ready to move him into the ward. A sigh of relief, and a warm feeling spreading all over my body. A victory!

No, I'm not that lucky. Miracles happen very infrequently. It could be a different picture: the blood pressure seventy and falling, the blood dripping freely through the drainage tube. "Why haven't you called me?" "We thought—." "Idiots, who told you you could think?" Probably this is exactly how it is. My heart is uneasy. I know there is no precognition. All those telepathic notions have never been scientifically proved. And yet. Let's hurry.

I open the door timorously. One look, and I see everything.

No, nothing dramatic has happened, one way or another. The scene is peaceful. A mere routine. Sasha is breathing by himself even though the oxygen tube is still in his mouth. His eyes are half-closed. It seems to me that his lips are not as blue as they were before, but this might be the electric light.

Dima is again sitting next to Oxana. Let them, she is a fine girl and they'll make a good couple. The electric impulses are racing across the monitoring screen measuring the heartbeats. Genya is sitting on a low stool counting the blood drops in the tube with a stop watch; there is a great deal of blood in the bottle. Perhaps they haven't emptied it for some time? Lenya is writing something in the journal. There is no one else in the room.

"All right, let's have it!"

Dima jumps up, embarrassed. He hasn't noticed my entrance. All right, Dima, I haven't noticed anything either. I was young myself, once.

"The pulse fluctuates between a hundred and ten and a hundred and thirty. The blood pressure ninety, and steady. Genya, how many drops?"

"Forty, but it was sixty before. For an hour and a half after the restart of the heart, almost three hundred cubes."

"And a little more precisely?"

"Two hundred and eighty-five."

"Do you consider this normal?"

"No, but it seems to decrease. I don't think this is really alarming."

"You don't think!"

Silence. I'm thinking. Perhaps really this is not too bad. There hasn't been much time. The bleeding may well stop by itself. Especially as there has been a decrease in the flow.

"Have you released urine?"

"Yes, about fifty cubes. Very dark."

Can it be that we shall now have kidney trouble? However, for an hour and a half this might be sufficient.

"Have you administered antihemorrhage drugs?"

"Of course. Here are the charts."

"I don't need them. I trust you."

I trust, but not always. That is why they push their charts at me. Generally, I trust them. They are fine youngsters, but they don't like paper work. And anyway, supervision never hurts. Blind trust alone is never enough, it's an invitation to carelessness. They all have enough selfless devotion for a three-night bedside vigil, but often not enough perseverance for a properly written case history. Don't they realize the importance of records? Indeed, it is difficult to compare a patient and a piece of paper. No comparison, but paper is also important. This is an element of organization without which no proper work is possible.

All right, enough of bookkeeping. What's to be done about the hemorrhage? This is our most pressing problem, even though both the heart and kidneys are still in grave danger.

"Do you have sufficient blood for transfusion?"

"Yes. Enough."

"Let's wait an hour, then get together and discuss the situation. Don't remove the tube from the trachea. Keep him under sedation."

I go out. I don't want to stay there. There is nothing to talk about, and there is nothing I can do to help. Shall I go through the wards? No, I don't want to do that either. I can't get over Sasha, and I hate to see more suffering tonight. Even thinking about surgery makes me feel sick. I am probably not suited for this work. Fool, it's much too late to think about that! To talk to Raya perhaps, to encourage her a little? And what about that other one, Irina? Well, I'm caught. Really caught. In fact at the moment I don't give a damn about either of them. All my resources of compassion for today have been exhausted. I'm dry.

And so, back to my room.

But what to do there?

First, let's eat this fruit salad. There is such a bitter taste of tobacco in my mouth. I always smoke like a chimney after operations.

Cherries, apples, a tasteless concoction, not homemade. Not important. It goes well with the roll.

That letter . . . Love. It is good to grow old and withdraw from it all. Much quieter, more comfortable. Perhaps it is too early for me? No, I wouldn't want it.

Enough of emotional upheavals . . . Unpleasant memories . . . "What! Soak stale bread in water again? Keep digging!" There was a morbid wartime anecdote like that about a man, tired of life, facing a firing squad before an open grave and offered a chance of life imprisonment in exchange for a confession.

One can get tired even of love.

Read the notebook? I'm afraid to touch it, in my mind it is already associated with that awful moment—"The heart's stopped!" It's terrible even to remember it. Nonetheless, we did start the heart up! Otherwise I could have been home already. With an empty head and despair in my soul. Both those women, Raya and Irina, would have been in hysterics. Yes, so far it has turned out well. He *is* alive. Am I sure that everything will be all right? No, a peaceful scene in the theater does not deceive me. Anything may happen yet. Anything and everything: another stoppage, unstoppable hemorrhage, second operation, heart failure. Frantic massage. "The pupils have already been enlarged for ten minutes!" Death. Another possibility: the hemorrhage has been arrested, but the amount of transfused blood causes kidney insufficiency. Death on the third day. Full consciousness to the very end. The eyes: "Can anything be done at all?" Nothing.

Enough. No point in exaggerating. The valve is good. If the insertion were not satisfactory, he would have been dead by now.

Let's take a look at that notebook nonetheless. For instance, about love. Fears are really superstitions.

I riffle through it. Here it is: "Programs of love . . ."

This has been written fairly recently, since it is almost at the end of the book and written at length. It means that he was no longer in love with Irina when he wrote it, if one believes his letter. The sober outlook of a scientist.

"First. The innate program of the sex instinct as a part of a more general urge of propagation of species . . ."

This is clear. This instinct persists in all living things; otherwise life would have ceased long ago on this planet. It wouldn't be easy to create complex organisms in a test tube even though they say that theoretically this is quite possible.

"The model of this program rests in the endocrine system, primarily in the sex glands and in the cerebral centers. This model is very complex and involves the centers of feeling and movement, the whole set of complicated mechanical programs activated by regulatory spheres of the entire organism.

"In animals this program is connected with seasons, and once activated it is not arrested even by the self-preservation instinct until the final fulfillment."

Yes, stronger than death.

However, one must not consider the sex instinct in animals as a mere urge to engage in copulation. This is love in the full sense of this word, a special psychological state producing profound changes in the entire behavior. It's a nightingale's song and nuptial dances of certain animals. It is self-denial.

I will skip some details given by Sasha, they are much too well known. It is strange, he can be both very profound, and also trite and shallow, even primitive in his approach. The tendency for oversimplification, purely mechanical clarity, without a true research foundation. Of course, working in a hospital bed with death staring you in the eye, one cannot be expected to go into any deep research; one must work, so to say, by touch.

Here is, for instance, Sasha's diagram of the human being:

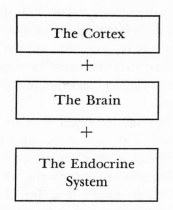

The Cortex

+

The Brain

+

The Endocrine System

Let's see what this means:

"In the human being there is a close correlation of all three components activating this particular program. Both the activation and arrestation depend on all three. Love as emotion originates in the cortex, then is passed to the brain, but becomes active only if supported from below, from the endocrine-gland system.

"First there appears longing, indefinite agitation, still unconscious searching. Vague interest in the opposite sex. These cerebral progams can be greatly stimulated by outside influences, books, pictures, conversations, et cetera. Gradually the search becomes conscious. Here we notice various changes in psychology: stimulation of some programs, inhibition of others. All this comes from the brain and is stored in the unconscious.

"Selection of the object . . ."

Damn, how prosaic all this sounds! I don't feel like

reading on. Of course, all this is correct: cerebral models of ideals, plus irritation and stimulation from the sex glands. But is this the way to describe falling in love? (Why not soaring to love?) What poetry, what purity, what fragrance. And after all this, "programs . . ."

"The next stage: a swift torrent of impulses from the cortex to brain to the endocrine system. The program develops swiftly. This is love. Meetings, intellectual discussions, still clean intentions. The cortex colors this program in magnificent hues. One should not think that this state is limited only to human beings." (Ah, I'm glad he sees this!) "A nightingale, for instance, can go through this stage just as acutely. They say that he is capable of actually dying of love.

"Caress comes next. New receivers are connected, new emotions, new programs come into play involving physical motions, both innate and acquired. Gradually the endocrine system begins to take over. Emotional contact is no longer sufficient, it loses its power of stimulation and becomes a habit. At a certain level of this stage, desire comes in, a very concrete set of physical programs. This is the climax. After that, a unique sense of sexual gratification and profound physical and emotional satisfaction.

"But . . . this also begins to grow into a habit. This is based on a certain law governing the nervous system. Also, the endocrinal influence undergoes certain changes. The stimulation from below does not reach the brain as rapidly as before, and the exciting of the cortex becomes difficult. This is the critical period: here comes the reappraisal of the object on the basis of previously adopted criteria of beauty, charm, intellect. If this trial is not passed successfully, the braking influences are applied from above. The reaction of the brain centers diminish to the minimum, and this is the end of love. For a while passion still can be agitated from below, through physical sex stimuli, temporarily invoking the long-forgotten programs; but the result is not satisfaction, but irritation.

"Contrariwise, if the partners have passed the trial of reappraisal, then love enters a quiet stage, is periodically activated by both the brain and gland systems and may last very long."

But is this love?

"It is impossible to determine all the levels of love, because the variations are endless. The sensuous and intellectual elements are intermingled differently in each individual. This is typical of all forms of behavior combining both the animal and social programs of behavior.

"Which is stronger then, the cortex or the lower levels, cerebrum and hormones? The brain, unquestionably. Animal passions cannot unite two intelligent human beings permanently, and can only periodically inundate all cerebral programs.

"Love is a physical urge, just like hunger and thirst, only more complex. All three can produce profound psychological changes. Love evokes the most pleasurable feelings and therefore man, trying to model it in his brain, has endowed it with romantic qualities. Generally it is a positive factor in society, but care must be exercised in order to restrain it from becoming a socially harmful phenomenon. Sex education is an all-important factor, since sex is a tremendous force and must be handled intelligently. It should not be suppressed, but overstressing it is a definite danger. This danger exists in all animal programs which must be handled with wisdom lest they spread into all spheres of human behavior and make the task of building the future ideal society all but impossible."

Generally, a well-written chapter. However I notice that he is avoiding the question of fidelity. The reason for infidelity rests probably also in animal programs, and only brain can guide one here. Again, the question of education. Education of emotion.

"The programs of love are different in men and women." Naturally. Women bear children.

"Love should not be equated with the sex act, even though this act is the direct result or, rather, logical conclusion of it. Here again, the brain as a powerful model-producing installation, creates a series of different programs which are responsible for all gradations in love from platonic adoration to brutal sensuous contact."

Enough for a while. When love is described in the language of programs and structures it loses all its charm. This is why artists are so opposed to cybernetics. Sasha holds that this is because the computers are not yet sufficiently developed. They are not perfected enough to compete with living systems. But all this is a matter of time. Probably it is something which he writes about in some other chapter.

However, I don't feel like reading this any longer. Time creeps by like a snail. Go back and check? Again, I don't feel like it. One must have patience and not dash in and out all the time. Otherwise one will not notice all the changes.

Hemorrhaging. The lowered coagulation level, or some small vessel broken during the massage? Unfortunately all our analyses don't give us a completely accurate picture of coagulatory processes. This is also a very complicated program. There is no point in guessing. Very well. We have decided to wait an hour, so let's wait.

And only twenty minutes have passed so far.

Shall I speak to Irina? I feel very guilty here. Besides, I would like to know what Sasha intends to do if he recovers. I don't suppose he'd need my advice, but still—

And the letter? Must I give it to her under any circumstances as he told me to do? Perhaps I have some right to decide this. Yes, I definitely have a right. Obviously I must speak to her. Or postpone it a little? All right, I'll see her and simply tell her about Sasha.

I go into the hall, knock at the door and say quietly: "You can come in now."

Is she asleep? I don't think so.

In a moment I hear the creaking of the laboratory door and in another moment she appears in my room. I will try to be kind to her, to smooth over my previous roughness. It is not her fault that she has fallen in love with a married man.

"Please sit down."

She sits down stiffly, silently, looking at me with cold censoring eyes, like a Madonna.

"Relax. His condition has improved."

I wanted to say, "is quite satisfactory," but caught myself in time. Superstition. Stupid, but true.

For a moment she sags and even closes her eyes. But then she sits up straight again. Fine self-control.

I turn on the desk lamp and switch off the overhead light. Let her face be in shadow. It is not necessary for anyone coming in to see her, and to recognize her later. They might want to know who she is. Well, just an acquaintance. Is it possible that she has never been in this clinic to see him? That means he does not love her at all. Well, that is rather evident from the letter.

I will hold the letter back for a while. In his notebook he explains his theories about animal programs, who knows, it might all come back to him if his health improves sufficiently. Or is it better for him if it doesn't come back? Probably. Shall I give the letter to her then? No, I'd better wait. I don't think much about Raya, she's hardly the wife for a man like Sasha, but there is Serezha, and there is nothing anyone can do about that. He can't escape that responsibility, not completely, in any event. That is my opinion, even though not everyone shares it. Could a situation like this be solved mathematically? Sasha would have said yes.

Let me talk to her.

"So far there isn't very much I can tell you. He wakes up now and then. He looked at me quite consciously."

I suppose she would have given much to have him look at her. He probably knew once how to look at her.

Briefly I tell her about the operation and about everything which has happened since. I try to be factual, suppressing all emotion. She sits silently, stiff, as though made of stone. Only her eyes are alive.

"Please tell me what can be expected in the immediate future. I must know everything. Don't be afraid, I can bear it."

Yes, obviously she knows how to keep herself in check. But what can I tell her when I don't know myself? But let's try to be gentle; I don't feel so terribly anguished any more. I know he is lying down there alive, and that his blood pressure is about one hundred. And that all the very dangerous time barriers have been safely overcome. Therefore I am now kind, patient, and can explain everything.

"There are several spheres of danger. First, the weakening of the heartbeat. This can happen, even though I don't anticipate a second heart stoppage. Tomorrow and the day after we may face decompensation, but probably not in an acute form as before. Second, the hemorrhage. Unless it stops soon a rather critical situation will arise. We shall know this tonight. The third danger, the weakening of kidney function because of hemolysis, the destruction of red corpuscles. This we shall also know fairly soon, by urination. Those are the main points, but there might be any number of unforeseen complications."

A pause. "You will not leave?"

For a moment I feel anger stirring inside me. I don't like it when people trust me more than is necessary. But Sasha is alive. So I control myself:

"I'll stay here tonight, for as long as is required."

What else can I talk to her about? But I see she is deeply disturbed, she has probably gone through agony these few days. It is quite possible that I am the only one who knows about their affair. She has no one else she can turn to.

Raissa Sergeyevna can cry openly and people will try to comfort her. But this one must control her anguish. No one can measure love and tell which one is suffering more. However, theoretically this must be possible. All emotions produce changes in the system. They can be measured, but this isn't easy, a problem for the future.

This damned cybernetics has stuck in my mind. Here you have a human being, a good woman who suffers cruelly, and you are trying to reduce her suffering to figures. Yes, if Sasha survives, he will definitely make me abnormal, like himself. I remember his letter.

There she sits staring into space, her eyes full of suffering. She should talk a little, unburden herself. This would help her. And I must know more about her in order to decide about the letter.

"Tell me about yourself."

An instant protesting move. But I cut it off.

"Please don't get your back up. I'm a doctor and a close friend of Sasha's. I have the right to know something about this side of his life."

A quick look, searching, appraising, slightly distrustful. I look back with quiet, serious eyes trying to assume the kindest possible expression. Quite sincerely. And in the back of my mind a quick thought: She is beautiful. A reflex from my younger days. It probably lives in a man until very old age. But it is not supported from below and therefore does not produce any behavior program. But I'm slightly ashamed of myself anyhow.

"Go ahead, tell me. It will make it easier for you."

She makes a move across the desk, toward me. Another look and I feel something tickling me between the shoulder blades; this often happens to me listening to music or poetry.

"I love him. I love him very much. Very much."

She drops her head. I can't see her eyes any more, only her long lashes. This is melodramatic. A pause.

"He is going away from me. And I'm desperately unhappy."

A quick impulse to tell her, "Fight for him!" But

Sasha is sick, any excitement is dangerous for him; this is not the kind of advice a doctor should give. No, I can't help her, except to listen to her sorrow.

"Tell me."

There is bitterness in her voice:

"What can I tell? A rather trite story, if one looks at it from the outside. It is unusual only to me. All right. I am thirty-two. A university graduate, a psychologist. Working at one of the institutes. A science candidate."

A thought: Sasha's theories; that's where it all comes from, Freud.

She pauses, and then continues evenly. The ice is broken.

"My childhood and youth were quite good. My father was a well-known engineer who died a few years ago. My mother died even earlier. I was left with my brother, a few years younger than I. He got married and has drifted away from me. Perhaps it is my imagination, but this is painful to me. We were such good friends."

Another pause.

I am listening, casting quick glances now and then in the direction of the door. Are they coming for me? Some twenty-five minutes more must have gone by.

She continues after a little sigh, as if overcoming an obstacle.

"I was also married. In my second year in university, very young. Love lasted for a year, then it was gone. We tried to overlook this for a couple of years more, then parted friends. No children. I was glad then, but now I regret it. Actually my husband was a good man, and I still respect him. I just don't know what happened, love just disappeared as if it had never been there at all. A person becomes a stranger, and everything about him begins to irritate you. Forgive me, like many women, I like to talk too much . . . If you must leave, tell me."

"No, I'll go in ten or fifteen minutes, unless they call me sooner."

A thought: She is really remarkably beautiful, without any sexual considerations. The reflex is smothered. But Sasha has good taste.

"I graduated ten years ago. Do you know what psychology is?"

"Only superficially. Mostly from novels."

"Well, psychologists probably know just as little. There are two schools; one based on philosophy, another on physiology. The first group works primarily with quotations, the second attempts to experiment. And since they were hit by Pavlov twenty years ago, they can't recover. And only very recently, actually within the last two years or so, there have appeared new influences and attempts to develop some exact method of investigation."

I have heard all this from Sasha. Even some words are his. Or is it vice versa? I don't think so.

"I was a good student and became very keen. I worked on some stupid thesis for four years, I'd been investigating the processes of attention among our students. At first I was terribly interested, our professor seemed like God to me. He knew so much and lectured so well. Don't think there was anything romantic in this, he was quite old. I defended my thesis in this institute, and at this point I started to grow cold toward our science. Understood that it was nothing but affectation and complicated terminology. Neither a clear hypothesis, nor precise methods. Actually we are just marking time. Spending hours in conversation. This became annoying to me, but I myself could not offer anything, neither a new theory, nor any original approach. I don't fool myself about my abilities."

(And I am thinking: Here is your main problem, my dear woman, and no one can help you. There are women like this, intelligent, even brilliant, but without a creative spark. Some of my best assistants are like that. Some of them will become professors, but they'll never originate anything. But wait . . . have you yourself brought in anything new? Well, anyway . . . Yes, yes, "anyway"! So let's listen.)

"Four years ago I lost all taste for work. I was just going to the institute, walking around, writing a few articles a year so that they would not fire me and take away my salary. Whatever you say, the pay scale of an advanced science worker is not that of a simple teacher. I was living strangely then. Probably quite well. I went to theaters and concerts, never missing a single appearance of any foreign artist. I had a good, smart set of friends, jounalists, artists, or simply clever people. I was reading Polish and German books, I know both those languages from my mother. It was quite pleasant, and rather empty. I had some . . . well, close male friends, but none of those things lasted. But I had never had any real happiness. Sometimes in the evening I would get so depressed I wouldn't know what to do with myself. And then I started thinking and realized that things could not go on like this."

Another pause. A very short one.

"Well, anyway, by the time Sasha appeared in our institute two years ago, I was ready to leave, to become a teacher, to get married, to have a bunch of children and start raising a family. With years, instincts had become stronger, I could not look calmly at a child in the street. And I almost stopped going out—lost all interest in social life . . .

"As you probably know, he was then involved in the theory of modeling psyche. His general method is also known to you: first he works everything out in his head, sometimes quite roughly, develops his theories and theses, and only then starts reading literature on the subject and talking to others. He came to the institute with some general hypotheses in order to sharpen them in discussion with psychologists. He gave three lectures, and of course charmed everyone, especially women and the very young. We women accept things through our emotions, especially when a man is so good-looking. His health was still quite good then."

"No, it wasn't good at all. But he kept his illness a secret."

"Yes? Well, then he did this very well. I learned about his heart condition only half a year after . . . after we became close friends."

I am thinking about various physiological things. Is she unobservant or just inexperienced?

"He had no particular success in our institute. We applauded him, but when it came to discussion there was no meeting of minds. Different approaches, different terminology. So he left with a firm belief that we were idiots. And our learned professors called him a charlatan, or mildly, a dilettante. But seeds had been planted, and some of us started to go to his institute to his classes, or just to talk to him. That was very interesting. He was so different from the dry skeptics among my friends, or from our professors. He had logic, clarity, and faith. Yes, faith in science, in the unlimited future of humanity. Faith based on firm theories and beliefs, real faith.

"I fell in love quickly, and completely. How could it be otherwise? He knew it. I didn't even try to conceal it. We started to meet in parks, libraries, theaters. Then he started to come to me. I was living alone with my brother—father was already dead, and we had a large flat. Forgive me for telling you these details. But my love was complete and real, I am not a little girl. We had talked a great deal. He had told me so much that was original and intelligent, more than I had heard in my first thirty years."

My dear woman, but you are in love! Of course, no matter what he says is clever and remarkable to you. Especially because this is often true. It is satisfying to think that he will continue to live . . . I wonder how the hemorrhage is? And the urine?

She is gazing into space and probably sees her old Sasha there.

"I think he also loved me then. Not the way I did, but enough. It was enough for me. This was a sort of honeymoon for us. I took a new interest in science, started to read books on cybernetics, study mathematics. I tried to keep up with him. He selected a theme for a thesis for me, and I fought for it tooth and nail. Our students laughed at me a little, they all knew about Sasha, but generally they were sympathetic. The thesis was accepted. It was titled 'The Psychology of Aesthetics in the Cybernetic Interpretation.' A cumbersome title, but my aim was to spread Sasha's theories into the arts. I am still involved in this work, it still holds me. But nevertheless I'm a woman, and probably a fool, because without him my work loses its grip on me. I often think that I'd trade all this for just an opportunity to be his wife, bear his children and iron his shirts. Perhaps I would get tired of all this quickly, but this is how I feel now."

I am thinking: Of course you'd get tired. You, our Soviet women, do not even realize what great advances you have made, and how infinitely more interesting and intelligent you are than the women of the West. For instance, why should my wife work? We have no servants, and there is a lot to do around the house and certainly enough money. But she comes from her clinic often later than I. She gets tired, she grumbles, but she would never trade her work for leisure. "Not interesting!" Quite right. Good woman.

"In my mind I knew that my love was hopeless, but in my heart I continued to believe in it. In my imagination I pictured various scenes of our mutual domestic bliss. As if some catastrophe had happened, and his wife was no longer with him. Various pictures, some of them brutal. But then I would shake my head and say, 'Idiot!' At that time I thought that he really loved me, that he wanted to become a part of my life. I introduced him to some of my friends, and saw that he was jealous. I was so happy! I thought it was a proof. But he didn't like my friends. I remember he said, 'small fry.' Perhaps I made a mistake. I don't know."

She is silent now, sad. I too remain silent. A minute. Two minutes.

"Irina Nikolayevna, perhaps you will tell me all?"

She waves her hand, a gesture of utter defeat and bitterness. How expressive some gestures can be! A throaty voice, a good actress.

"There is nothing to tell."

But then, after a brief pause, she decides to continue. Perhaps just to be able to stay here, and not to be alone. This is simply for me. Without any spirit.

"Our happiness did not last long. If one could call that happiness." A tone of bitter irony. "A stolen happiness, you understand?"

Associations. Memories. Yes, I understand.

"Of course, I couldn't keep up with him. I tried, I read, I worked. But then I started to notice that he was not with me. You know how I like to talk. I would stop suddenly, look at him and understand that he was far away, not even listening. That would be only a moment, he would collect himself and become tender and attentive again. But I saw all, understood all. I knew that he was withdrawing from me, and I was in despair. I didn't know what to do. You know how it happens in dreams. Someone very dear to you is going away, disappearing, you run after him, stretch your arms, cry. And he is gone. You fall on the ground, weeping, and wake up. Then you walk half a day under the spell. It is the same thing now. Only I won't wake up."

She sighs. A brief silence. Her eyes become moist, but then she pulls herself together and they are dry again.

I too am silent. What can I say? I have never developed the professional knack of consoling brokenhearted relatives. I am sorry for them, but the right words don't come to me easily.

She continues:

"Actually this is the end of the story. This coincided with his illness, or rather with his relapse, as you tell me. But I don't think that was the cause."

I instantly remember his letter, his notebook. His description of love.

"You are mistaken. This could very well be the direct cause. I don't believe in disembodied love among adult people."

And my thought: He simply couldn't. This led to a belief in his insufficiency. He was too proud to admit it and wanted to escape. And even the emotional cooling off was probably connected with his physical debility. I wonder how it was with them on the purely intellectual plane? It works sometimes, but not often.

"And how did your own work progress?"

"I was trying hard. Of course, when he started to draw away, my capacity for work started to diminish. I thought more about him than about my theories. But still, my work was progressing. I had read literature on the subject, spoken to some scientists, some art specialists. And of course, to Sasha. Certainly if I ever achieve anything, it will be his thoughts in my words. I think that eventually I shall finish it. Of course, just as soon as I sensed his estrangement, I altered my behavior. I stopped talking about emotions, avoided all physical contact. I had become just a friend to him. And I think he likes that."

Another brief pause.

"About my work I will tell you some other time; as a scientist you can even help me. But now you have no time, and I no inspiration. If, of course, it interests you at all."

I thank her politely and assure her that I am interested, and this is sincere. I like this woman, I like being with her, listening to her.

"Tell me the truth, Professor. What will happen to Sasha? I mean, if he gets well? Please believe me this interests me not merely on a personal level. We were in love, it is all gone, and there's nothing anyone can do about that. But he is an unusual man, I even go as far as to say that he is a sort of genius."

"Now you have gone too far!"

"No, I haven't. I have spoken to mathematicians, they value his work very much. And his scope? Mechanics, medicine, psychology, sociology, art, he puts something new, something fresh into everything."

"You mean, cybernetics?"

"Yes, of course, but it's more than that. I've got tired of that word. I think Sasha has outgrown it."

"All right, let's not quarrel over words. Genius, talent or just a gifted man, is that so important? The important thing is that he can contribute a great deal to humanity."

"Very well. But will he ever be well enough to do it?"

"I must tell you the truth, I don't really know. But I don't think he'll ever have his health back absolutely. Creeping rheumatism, secondary changes in the liver, they can't be cured by a new valve. Or can they? Our science is very approximate. I am not so sure about the valve itself either. Will it prove durable enough to last for many years? It might grow in and become covered with living tissue, but it also might start dissolving. It should hold up for three to five years. And during these years we shall look for new valves, for new methods. Everything in science is going slowly, but it is not static."

"And how would he have to live?"

"Under a glass jar. I think that the most important thing for him is to be able to work. His physical exertion must be very limited. It doesn't mean that he must stay in bed, but everything must be rigidly controlled. And, of course, his emotional life must be even more limited. Excitement is more dangerous for him than anything else. His very work involves a certain degree of emotional excitement, but that can't be curtailed. Otherwise he would become useless to himself."

I am watching her attentively. Does she understand that I am speaking about her, that I am telling her that love is an impermissible luxury for him? That it would destroy his capacity for work, and might even kill him? Like all ignorant people, Irina probably believes that a new valve will make him as good as new, and that their love may be resumed. And here I'm reading a death sentence to this hope. I can't help it. I have no right to give her any false encouragement. It is enough that I'm not giving her that letter. She may not believe what I say if she doesn't want to, and of course she doesn't. But she is brave.

"Very well. Everything is clear. And what would you advise me to do?"

Now I must think a little. Tell her simply, "You must forget him"? No, this is too direct. To give her some hope? I don't want to. Even though I think that she has a definite chance. When his physical strength returns, love might flare up again. Not like before, of course, but still—all depends on her cleverness. She has enough beauty, and perhaps other assets, to achieve this. But if she is foolish, it's hopeless. She is very beautiful, but that does not prove intellect. I shall give her an honest answer:

"I don't believe that you should build your life round any hope for his love. If he loves you, nonetheless he is a sick man, and any emotional burden would shorten his life. Therefore, rely on yourself. From my own experience I know that there are two strong anchors, work and children. But even they don't provide automatic happiness. Work must be creative and in some degree your own. Forced labor is appalling. Happiness must be earned. It is the same thing with children. To get happiness out of them, you must bring them up. You must put into it not only love and care, but a great deal of effort. I understand this in the case of my granddaughter, Lenochka. Not my daughter, I was young then and stupid. If you have children and work that you love, everything else can be handled, infidelity, loss of love, material difficulties, career upheavals."

"But I have no such anchors! I'm not sure about my work, and I have no child, even though I want one. What shall I do?"

"Fight. First of all, stick to your work. It seems to me that it's very interesting. You must think and think about it, and then new horizons will open up for you. I'm sorry I'm using such banal expressions, but I can't find others for the moment. And the child must be born."

"How? I can't be with . . . with anyone else. I simply physically can't!"

Strange creatures, women. I could never understand this "simply can't" of theirs.

"Then adopt one. But be sure that he is very young. I am sure that education is responsible for ninety per cent of our emotions. Yours or someone else's, you'd love him just as well."

"It is easy to say. No, I shall wait a couple of years."

"Of course, you still have time. But remember that it flies."

"I must thank you for your advice, but actually I knew all this myself. But it's difficult for me to live. You understand, I've no backbone for life. I envy you. I envy even Sasha, despite his condition. I envy many women I know, simple women with husbands and children. You all know what you want, but I don't. I'm drifting."

"Too bad for you, my dear. All those you envy have simply convinced themselves that what they have is what they want. If you don't follow their example and you continue to doubt, you will end up by having a miserable old age. One must choose."

"I will try."

A pause. All is said. It is ten o'clock. The hour has gone, even five minutes more. Shall we be able to stop the hemorrhage? I don't know. Something inside tells me that we will. But I don't trust presentiments. They have fooled me so many times before.

"Irina Nikolayevna, I must go to the operating theater. You can stay here, if you want, or go back to the laboratory, and wait there."

She takes the hint and rises. Her face and eyes are complicated. Grief, hurt . . . she probably feels that she's not understood and not sympathized with. Or maybe this is just my imagination? Maybe she's just tired? Well, just as she likes.

I walk with her to the laboratory door. She has the key. The hall is deserted. I return to my room and smoke a cigarette before going to Sasha.

8

STEPAN

AGAIN THE CORRIDOR, the stairway. It is now night. The clinic is quiet. Only in the interns' room there is a sound of conversation. The voice of Oleg. Of course. He can never keep it down.

How long will I have to walk up and down like this? Up to my office, down to the theater. Perhaps everything is all right there. Doubtful. Major surgery has destroyed my sense of optimism. Nothing is easy. Everything must be fought over, torn out with your teeth. Shall I stop and see Raya? No, I don't feel easy about that. Just spoken to Irina, and now to the wife? How would I look at her, try to comfort her? But why not? It is all Sasha's doing, not mine. Still, I feel that now I am a sort of accomplice. But what could I do, send that poor woman away? Hard to tell. The problem of good and evil, of virtue and sin.

I enter the operating theater. No particular picture of happiness. Sasha is breathing by himself, but through the oxygen tube. Dima is near his face looking down, checking on his pupils I imagine. Near the ampoule connected with the drainage tube, Lenya, Petro, Genya, all crouching. Maria Vasilievna is hovering over them with a stopwatch. Clearly they are counting blood drops. It means that the hemorrhage is continuing. The main problem remains unsolved.

Pay your debts, my friend. What debts? What have I done? Stepan perhaps? Or is it Sasha who is paying for Irina with his blood? Needless questions. The subconscious sense of guilt is universal. Everyone is a debtor to everyone else. The interdependence of guilt.

I wait until they finish the count. Then:

"Well?"

Petro volunteers a report:

"Everything is in order. Only the hemorrhage continues, just as before."

"Everything's in order! You're an incorrigible optimist. There's just one hitch: your patients are dying too often."

He is silent, hurt. A tactless remark, perhaps, but now I'm annoyed with the whole world. How long can a man suffer? Just take a look: a continuing hemorrhage, a prospect of repeated operation. Open the wound, look for the bleeding vessel, which you probably won't find anyway, because this is a general oozing from many vessels due to the lowered coagulation factor of the blood. This means anesthesia again and again the danger of heart stoppage. Again this, and again that! I feel sick even thinking about it, I just have no strength left. A momentary lightninglike thought: Why didn't he die at once? Then a sense of horror—am I a monster even to allow a thought like that to enter my head?

"How many drops?"

"About fifty now. It falls off and increases periodically. In the last half hour, one hundred and twenty cubes."

A quick calculation. This means, about two hundred and fifty per hour. Six liters per twenty-four hours. It means that an equal amount must be replaced by transfusion. With damaged liver and kidneys this is practically fatal. And where would we get so much fresh matching blood?

"The coagulation level?"

"Clots are forming at six minutes, but not particularly firm."

"Have you administered everything according to the chart?"

"Yes, here's the record."

Dima gives it to me. A long one, everything is recorded to a second. I'm checking it. Yes, everything has been done to improve coagulation. But can anyone guarantee that there is not one bleeding vessel somewhere? Has this not happened before? Especially possible because the heart had been massaged through the closed chest during the occlusion.

I'm standing there, thinking. As always thoughts are coming in on several levels at the same time. The main one: What to do now? Open the wound, or wait? Of course, eventually the hemorrhaging will stop, but how to wait through this, and what will happen then? An operation, even if no single source of bleeding is found, usually helps. You can always tie up a vessel here, burn it down there, and then the system somehow generally reacts positively to repeated surgery. But—oh God, how afraid I am to cut those stitches open! To see that heart again, to feel its contractions under my fingers! And to expect every second that each is the last one. "Defibrillator! Massage!" No, I can't face it. I just can't face it. I haven't the strength at the moment.

The thoughts on the second level: Irina is suffering in a dark laboratory. Raya in the waiting room downstairs. He doesn't love either one. They both probably know it. I know what this means, I had gone through this myself. But what are all those emotional sufferings compared to *this!* I'd be glad to go through love-and-jealousy torture for a year just not to stand here and try to decide what to do. No, I'm lying, a year is too much. One can go insane. I just don't know what's better, or worse.

Still another level: Everyone has wilted. It is eleven o'clock. Have they eaten anything? Well, probably nibbled at something. They are young. Appetites. I can go on and on without food, but what about them? "I" again!

All right, but what's to be done, anyway?

"What are the other showings?"

Dima:

"Not too bad. Pulse, one hundred and twenty-four; the blood pressure fluctuates between one hundred and one hundred and thirty. The venous, one hundred and forty millimeters. The density of venous blood was fifty, now it is fifty-seven."

"Urine?"

"Not very much. Lenya, show the bottle. This is the yield for the last half hour."

Lenya shows: about fifty cubes of dark liquid. I am afraid we might have trouble in this department. Actually, however, this is not too alarming. If it goes on like this, we may expect about two liters. This is sufficient.

"Go ahead."

"He woke up once and even became restless, we administered sedatives. Breathing, you can see for yourself: rather even, and he has been breathing by himself. If you decide not to . . . well, then we can extract the tube in a little while."

"How much blood have you in reserve?"

"Liuba will look. Liuba, please check in the refrigerator."

"How is it that you don't know yourself? You must be aware of this every minute you are here!"

"I've got a bit mixed up, Professor. I've just been checking on the entire loss and replacement. I believe we have about a litre left."

"You believe! You must know."

I'm jumping down his throat for no good reason. No, there is a reason. There have been occasions with this same Dima. "No more blood!"

Liuba comes back. She has calculated all the reserves. Even written them down. How thin she is, pale, traces of lipstick on her lips. A pretty girl, she likes to make up, but now she is too worn out to care. She can hardly move. Her robe is stained with blood, but she pays no attention.

"We have five hundred cubes of fresh blood, and about seven hundred and fifty of the old, ten days. Also there's some old blood of the first type group, and blood from the machine, but with high hemolysis."

"There's your litre!"

This situation is now clear. We must send for some fresh blood. But the main problem remains unsolved. I must decide what to do. Who can possibly take this burden off my mind? Nobody. This is my task. One can't take a vote on this, I am supposed to know better than anyone. Sasha's life is in my hands. A quick thought: Shall I wake him up and ask him? After all, this is his life. Stupid. He would not know what you're talking about. Ask Raya, or that other one, Irina? You're a fool, Professor. They are scared, unhappy women, and this is your friend. Is friendship a less meaningful relationship than sex? Perhaps less. Here is intellect; there, emotion. And which is more meaningful for him? I don't know. He has a highly overdeveloped intellect, and this hurts people who love him. Poor Irina.

Nonsense, she won't die. Or will she? Women like that can die of love, even in our rational age. Despite all her intellectual interests. She may decide to end it all. Didn't you feel the same way yourself?

No, this probability is not high. Irina will live, and so will Raya. And what about Sasha? I can't really evaluate. Of course, the odds have become better than they were this morning, but there are still plenty of dangers.

But anyway, what to do? Talk to the kids? Of course none of them can possibly think up anything new, because there is just nothing one can think of. A really accurate decision can't be made in view of the incomplete information and there is no way of getting more at the moment. However:

"Comrades, come here. Let's step out and talk this over. Dima and Oxana will stay here and watch the patient. It won't be long."

They are filing out, dragging their feet. Everyone is exhausted. We go to the interns' room. We find Oleg and Valya discussing something, there is so much tobacco smoke that one can cut it with a knife. Apparently they have got hold of a fresh supply of cigarettes.

Gradually the room is filling up. Even Stepan has appeared from nowhere. He feels that the "chief" is too preoccupied and too unhappy to jump at him. He is mistaken.

"Stepan Stepanovich, why haven't you gone home after your shift?"

"I'm watching Onipko. He is still critical, but there is an improvement."

I want to say something nasty, but I control myself. To hell with him, let him stay here. Expiation of sins. But just let him expiate his guilt, and there would be no getting rid of him. Personally I have nothing against him, a good man, intelligent. But how can I forgive him for neglecting our patients? Well, never mind. Later.

"All right, Comrades, you all know the situation. What do you suggest? Shall we operate now, or wait? And if wait, then what else can we do now?"

I know that they can't suggest anything which I don't know myself. I'm not exaggerating my intelligence, but I've had more experience than any one of them, and they have already done everything that could possibly be done while I was sitting up in my office, delving into Sasha's love life. We can administer this medication or that again, but this will hardly change the situation. And this is not a case to experiment on, it has probably been the most complicated operation we have ever performed in this clinic, taking into consideration the patient's condition. And then, and I must confess this openly, after all, this *is* Sasha. This makes any decision much harder, for me, in any event. I hate to guess and experiment in his case. Again we must deplore the limitations of our science and hope that cybernetics will change all this in the future. But I won't live that long. It is all nonsense.

Just as I expected. Petro:

"We can repeat the whole course of medications promoting coagulation."

Lenya:

"This has been done twice. What's the use of repeating something to which the patient does not respond? After all, this is not harmless. Of course, if the Professor decides against the operation, we shall repeat this later. We must count on the hemorrhage continuing at least until the morning, if not longer."

Semyon reports that our station has no more fresh blood of either the three- or the one-type group, and it must be sent for. And the old blood, obviously, would be harmful to Sasha.

"Then what do you suggest, surgery?"

"No, I suggest nothing. I am scared to death when I think of the possible second heart stoppage."

For a while there is silence. I am looking at all of them. There they are, all different, but all good. No one-hundred-per-centers, but each a valuable member of the profession. And I? Everyone tends to exaggerate his own importance. Sasha claims that good and evil can be accurately calculated if one approaches this problem from the standpoint of society. In the olden days this was simpler. Then Christians thought that in God's office there was a sort of computer for each person which automatically evaluated people's behavior, and then submitted the final figure for God's decision. It was more or less arithmetically decided. So-and-so went up, so-and-so down.

I see Stepan shifting his weight from one foot to the other near the door, dying to say something. I throw a straight questioning look in his direction:

"Well? Speak up."

"Professor, supposing we—*you*—try a direct blood transfusion?"

And immediately, before I can react:

"I have blood of the third group, hemoglobin eighty, and I'll be glad to donate."

We all look at him with amazement. This is an idea! We all feel a little taken aback, are we a bunch of idiots not to have thought of this simple thing sooner? There is such a method of arresting stubborn hemorrhaging—not simply fresh blood, but a direct transfusion from vein to vein, so as not to destroy anything even the most minute components. We have forgotten about it because we normally do not use it. We have tried it a few times in some very critical cases, but got no response and, after that, have generally discarded it. Needlessly. This is no guaranteed method, but some clinics claim definite positive results in some cases.

Oleg can't contain himself:

"Good man, Stepan! Genius! And you wanted to get rid of him, Professor!"

I am silent. The first happy reaction has already worn off. I mentally jumped at it, just like the rest, because it eliminated the necessity of an immediate decision, but now I am already considering the whole thing soberly. Basically, the suggestion is good. It just *may* help. But if it doesn't work, and there are many chances that it won't, there will be a certain loss of critical time. True, not much, we should see results quite quickly. Yes, a good suggestion. It annoys me a little that it was Stepan who has come out with it. Now, the amnesty is unavoidable. Not that I'm against it, but I'd like to arrive at it myself instead of being forced into it. It would be a good thing to take the blood from someone else; otherwise Stepan would instantly graduate into a hero. But that wouldn't be just and I can't allow that.

"Stepa, of course, is no genius, but none of us, alas, is a genius. Rather the contrary. We should have thought of this sooner, but we haven't and Stepa has, let's give the devil his due. It was a good suggestion, and I'm taking it. But you, Stepa, don't get the idea that after this you will go on bungling as much as you like. I shall watch you like a hawk, and I'll miss nothing, so don't have any hopes."

This perhaps is again a bit of unnecessary cruelty. God's electric computer is working through me.

"We have enough people here with the three-type blood, besides Stepan."

This is Maria Vasilievna, the merciless disciplinarian. Also, the conscience of the world. She would forgive anyone murdering her, but not a doctor neglecting a patient. She is right, there are enough prospective donors in this very room; but Stepan deserves preferential treatment, he is the author of the original idea. Besides, this must be important to him and not only for his self-rehabilitation in the eyes of his colleagues. He needs it for himself, to prove that he is not as worthless as he must have felt himself to be the whole day. Let him get the full dose.

"We shall take the blood from Stepan. Let's hope it will prove to be lucky."

"And that Sasha won't become stupid after that."

This is Oleg's contribution. He never loses his sense of humor even though his witticisms are not always very appropriate.

Everyone is happy.

The fact that surgery has been postponed is a great relief, and the choice of Stepan as a donor is also appreciated. I don't think there are many of us here really eager to play this part, after a day like the one we've had. Not because we are afraid, but no one likes pain. I for one dislike injections; the moment a needle touches me, I cringe. And this will be a very thick needle. Of course, if it is necessary, all of us would volunteer, but if there is another volunteer, so much the better.

And Stepan is fairly beaming. There is a theatrical streak in him; he likes effects. All right, let him have his fill. The important thing is the result.

"Oleg, you're the youngest, and the most energetic. You will handle the transfusion."

Oleg is the youngest of our senior doctors. He is not really very young, perhaps thirty, but he looks years younger, a mere boy. I even doubt that he shaves, though of course he must.

"But let's hurry, kids."

"What are we to do with the breathing tube? Shall we extract it?"

"I don't know . . . I think we'd better use slight gas anesthesia. It's harmless, and it's best for him not to wake up during this procedure. That might cause some psychological damage."

Everyone agrees. It will delay the final waking up, but one hour more or less does not make that much difference. Oleg energetically chucks away his cigarette butt and commands:

"All right boys. Finish your cigarettes and let's go. Stepa, when were you in the bathhouse last?"

"I take a shower every morning! Only missed today, because of the double shift."

"Tsk, tsk, such culture!"

A direct blood transfusion is a simple procedure.

There is a special set of tubes and gauges. A needle is inserted into the donor's vein, and also into one of the recipient's. The blood is transmitted by a special syringe, without the use of any anticoagulants used in conservation.

Oleg and Stepan go out, but we stay here. There is no point in rushing. The preparation will take at least half an hour.

As always during these night sessions, there is an acute cigarette shortage. We have to send Genya to my office, I still have two packs there. One is immediately picked to pieces.

The conversation now comes round to the surgical profession. Why has everyone chosen this clinic and this heartbreaking work?

Semyon:

"I like strong sensations during heart operations. Not in any other branch of medicine, or even routine surgery, is there so much excitement. When you hold a human heart in your hand, it is such a unique feeling."

True. Strong sensations attract many young people. In one period of my life I had been attracted by them as well. But now I feel sorry for patients who provide us with such sensations. There are some young surgeons who undertake practically hopeless operations for this kind of excitement. Not in our clinic; we watch against this very strictly.

But anyway one cannot discard this stimulus. For these sensations in the operating theater a surgeon is willing to pay with days and nights of hard thankless toil: ambulatory work, bandaging, writing up case histories, even talking to patients' relatives. Probably there is nothing morbid or evil in this. Semyon has already defended his candidate's dissertation, but it is not pure science which has brought him here. Operations. The romanticism of surgery.

Now Vasya, our aspirant, takes the floor. He is very young, with an obstinate chin. He will go far.

"I'm here to work on my dissertation. They offered to let me do this in our institute, but there it's all dead routine, appendices and fractures. Here, at least, there are new ideas, new methods, complicated operations."

This is the second stimulus of young doctors, to write quick theses. It is true that it is difficult to find a good theme working in a routine clinic; all of them have been used and reused. It does not mean that all the problems of general surgery have been solved; on the contrary, much is still very obscure and uncertain. Old methods have become antiquated, the new not yet fully developed. The routine clinics have no time for research; they can't study such problems as shock, infection, biological reactions, because there are not enough new ideas and no proper equipment. For this one needs large modern laboratories with all the costly new equipment; in medical research one can't work by touch.

In our clinic, as in all those of this type, we are breaking virgin soil. We are a showplace, and the government is generous with funds. We can experiment and study various diagnostic and physiological problems; in a place like ours it is much easier to find and develop a spectacular dissertation. Besides, all this is connected with exciting actual work; here we study, we teach, we allow young surgeons to show their initiative and operate. In fact one can quickly carve out a career from here, always providing that one has surgical talent.

Well, this is understandable. Doctors are also people, they want to get ahead, to make a career.

"Appendices and fractures must also be treated," Maria Vasilievna cuts in with an ominous calm.

"Sure, but that's not for me."

"Not for me either," Genya says. "I want to get to the very top of my profession."

Now Maria Vasilievna is outraged.

"I'm ashamed of you boys, shocked! One speaks about excitement, another pure science, the third, his dissertation, still another, his profession and his career! And where are the patients? Where are compassion and mercy? Where is the sense of service? Where is the noblest of professions?"

Direct questions. All are silent, a little taken aback by this attack. Yes, where is all that? Are our patients merely the material for theses, study, science? But this is not so with my kids. I know this definitely, I've been watching them. In any event, not completely so. I must support them.

"Maria Vasilievna, you're not just. There is the noble profession and there is compassion. Can't you see it? Look at them all sitting here, what do you think they are doing, writing dissertations?"

"Stop it, Professor, don't defend them. I think our youngsters don't have enough dedication. It is a profession to them, they don't really care what they are, physicians, agronomists, engineers. Medicine is not a profession, not in this sense. It is service. It must be and that's what they don't understand. And if they are sitting here, hungry and without tobacco, well, it proves nothing. Some of them are here because it's their duty, others because they are just curious, and some even because of you. If you went home now, many of them would disappear as well."

Embarrassment. Some, perhaps all, would like to protest, but Maria is a senior doctor here, they like and respect her and don't dare to argue with her.

Only Petro decides to speak. Very quietly:

"You, Masha, haven't examined their souls and you don't know what's going on there. Not everyone cries when people die, and not all brag about their compassion, but all our boys and girls—"

She interrupts him:

"Oh stop it, stop it! I know their souls very well. Sure, they work hard, but if anything happens in the ward, no one would think of sending a telegram to relatives so that they could come and find their dear one still living, not unless you remind them of it! And you— Oh, what's the use of talking! I'm going."

She gets up and leaves.

Petro smiles crookedly. "What a woman. What a sweet disposition."

Silence. Everyone feels uneasy.

I am thinking. Snatches of thought. There is something in what Maria said. Mercy. This word has gone out of fashion. Probably unfortunate. I'm not speaking about merciful God; but a sister of mercy, as they used to call nurses, was not bad at all. Once this was considered to be a great virtue, mercy. Now it has almost become equated with weakness and sentimentality. No one ever speaks about it as proof of a person's nobility.

Mercy and compassion as emotions have two sources. One is the instinct of propagation, especially in the case of children. Then, the instinctive transposition of "programs of suffering" upon oneself. It is true even about dogs, beat one, another whines.

But mercy is basically a natural reaction. When man, especially child, learns the basic ethics of social behavior this natural feeling can be highly developed. Not in an equal measure in everybody, but everyone is susceptible to it. The brain must support good instincts rather than rationalize them away.

This closely concerns us medical people who are constantly dealing with people's suffering. It would seem that compassion should grow and develop with each year of practice, but this unfortunately is not so in the majority of cases. Very unfortunate.

Getting used to it, getting accustomed. This is a remarkable mechanism, habit; the acclimatization of the system to strong irritants which at first produce violent reaction, but then gradually cease to act at all. These programs work starting at the level of a simple cell and ending with the most complex psychic functions. At first other people's suffering causes you pain, but then you get used to it as if it were your own pain, and learn to live with it. It doesn't bother you so much any more. Then comes a day when a doctor or a nurse notices that his sense of compassion has all but gone. Some would not admit this, but once you start thinking back and honestly remembering things, you will find this point in your own career. This is the normal defense mechanism. Only a few resist it, these few have overdeveloped compassion centers. These centers do not submit to habit. Such people are sorely tried if they have to work in a place like ours. True, they suffer, but they also experience the highest sense of happiness when they succeed in triumphing over death. This feeling is akin to a sudden release from cruel pain.

Unfortunately, patients themselves are doing much to smother the sense of compassion in doctors and nurses. When man performs some service, he expects a reward. He does not realize it perhaps, but he wants it. No money, no presents—those things only insult you—but some expression of gratitude, some emotional return. This greatly supports all the reflexes of compassion.

And I can't say that our patients are especially generous in this respect.

A doctor performs an operation, all has gone well, but when the patient is released he often forgets to thank or even go and say goodbye to his doctor. Most of them explain it by saying: "I knew how busy you were and I didn't want to waste your time." Of course, I am very busy and can't arrange any special thanksgiving audiences, but he, the patient, certainly could have found time to come, or even write a little note.

No point in talking about this. I am already old and I understand everything. And I don't condemn anyone, I have got over it. But younger doctors feel bitter about it, and for a good reason. In different economic systems the doctor's services are paid for with money, with us a few words of gratitude go a long way in making our work rewarding.

One old woman doctor, a brilliant gynecologist, who had worked for many years in the same town and had saved many women, once told me:

"I meet my former patient and I see her cross the street to the other side in order not to speak to me. She is avoiding me, hoping that I have not seen her, but I don't feel bitter about it. Just imagine that you have borrowed a great deal of money in an emergency and have no way of paying it back, and that your creditors don't demand it and don't even expect it. You are very grateful to them, but would it be easy for you to speak to them? It is a degrading feeling to be an insolvent debtor."

She was probably right, but it is difficult for young doctors to accept this philosophy. They want a return for their work. And I wanted it too, in the past.

Patients must understand that when a doctor saves a dangerously sick person he not only expends his time and effort, but puts into it a small part of his soul, which can be paid for only with gratitude. At least, a good doctor must give this part of his soul if he is a real physician and not a hack. And our patients often overlook this point.

It is so sad to watch how a chain of misunderstandings and mutual hurts often builds up between a doctor and a patient, eventually making them strangers and in some cases even enemies. Gratitude comes so hard to some people. Perhaps I look upon this with a bit of prejudice, but I can't help it. Doctors are also people and they have human weaknesses, they can't all be like Maria Vasilievna.

So how could I condemn my young doctors as she is doing? She cannot understand it, because her own centers of compassion have long since grown out of all proportion. Perhaps this is the only thing which sustains her in life, she has nothing at all besides her work, our clinic. She is unflinching in her selflessness and nobility. These people are necessary, they remain the living symbols of humanity, but it is unrealistic to expect everyone to be a saint.

However in one respect she is right, people without souls should not be admitted into our work. Our laws are too liberal in this respect. I don't advocate punishing medical careerists and egocentrics or putting them in jail; this is a crime but not a punishable one. It would be enough to revoke their permits to practice. Quite sufficient. Or at least they should be taken off actual hospital work and put into laboratories where their egotism could not hurt people.

Teacher and physician. Those are two professions in which love of people is an absolutely necessary qualification. And the government should be a little more generous with them.

I understand that there is a purpose in limiting their material returns in order to keep the undesirables out of this work, but they should receive at least as much attention and material comfort as the specialists who build machines.

"Well, children, do you suppose you've made a mistake in your choice of profession?"

Silence. Quite understandable. It is indelicate to speak about this. Especially when this question comes from the chief.

Well, I suppose I'd better go somewhere. There is no prospect of any engaging conversation here. They are all too tired and are still smarting from Masha's attack.

I kill my half-smoked cigarette and leave.

I don't want to go into the operating theater. I don't want to be in the way or create an impression that I'm checking up on them. They always do something wrong, and this irritates me. I am tired of forever fighting against some small imperfection. In the mornings I have enough energy for that, but not at night.

At this point I can't help Sasha in any way.

I also don't want to look at Onipko or any other critical case. There is Maria, there is Petro. Why should they have enough energy when I'm so played out? Well, Maria is tireless, and Petro is young. Probably nothing really terrible has happened there anyway. Otherwise I would have known.

To my room upstairs?

Irina is there. She would hear the click of the electric switch and listen behind the partition, what has happened to Sasha? I don't feel like talking to her now. There is nothing new I can tell her, and I have largely exhausted my sympathy for her tonight.

Where to, then? The balcony. Let's have another smoke. There are chairs and no one would see me there. The patients are now asleep. Or at least lying quietly in their beds. Many are awaiting some news of Sasha. Like Raya and Irina.

Darkness. Warmth. Peculiar spring air.

I am thinking back. Trying to remember conversations, events.

How different all my young doctors are. There are no two persons completely alike in the world, they are all alike and all different. The multiplicity of alikeness. There should be a mathematical term for this.

Programs of behavior, from Sasha's notebook.

A devilishly complex thing, this human behavior. There are so many people the behavior of whom I can't understand. Not only criminals. Those are extreme cases. Heroes. Loafers. Drunks. Good family men. Insensitive doctors. Half-insane inventors. Dreamers. And then, just people—going to work, coming home, watching television, bearing children, sleeping with their wives. Mostly honest, modestly dull, modestly cowardly, they love lukewarmly and hate the same way. What sustains them in life?

To each his own. Different programs of behavior.

Probably it is important to learn about those programs. Important for modeling. I am already juggling these terms as if they were my own.

It is important primarily in order to know oneself. To find some new ammunition for the battle of living. For happiness. Otherwise each of us is wandering in a trackless forest of passions and anguishes.

It is also important for society. To create a better community of men, to develop programs for a very complex system of which man is an integral part. This work cannot be replaced by just producing tons of steel or even grain.

Of course, men are different. Until recently this had been accepted as an axiom. All that one could do was to create a composite image of the average man, and taking him as a pattern, calculate distribution of material goods and moral principles.

Now this has been changed. Sasha and his friends say that their machines can write down the programs of all the different brains in the world and reduce them to mathematical formulas. One can record the thoughts and feelings of all men, arrange this material symphonically and play back the whole system, the model society. Obviously the existing computers can create only very crude models. And they can merely scratch the surface of the future. But even now they can arrange and calculate many more factors than a single human brain, or even a collection of many brains. This is true about medicine as well. Even the existing machines have widened our horizons tremendously, and when fully developed these diagnostic and therapeutic machines will probably come up with more accurate answers than a whole medical convention can do at present.

I don't know. It is hard to imagine a machine which can combine thousands of working intellects and temperaments, and then issue absolutely correct formulas for planning and governing. Daydreamers, these cybernetists!

I gaze round.

Clouds have covered the whole sky. Only on the horizon where the sun has set there is still a narrow band of roseate light.

What would happen to our town after an atomic explosion? It is so difficult to imagine children, buds on the trees, and *that*. One's mind refuses to accept such a combination.

This just cannot happen! Unfortunately it can.

America. Once a guiding light for everything new and progressive in the world. And now? I was there, I saw. Waves of cynicism, pessimism, sex, greed. Merciless exploitation of all the basest instincts. Of course, there are also men there who search, but it is a difficult climate for them. Twelve television channels and all preach the same thing: "Hit him! Kill him!" Children's stores full of toy weapons. Books in drugstores with tortured faces on multicolored covers. Violence. This poison spreads, it engulfs youth, children, everybody. All this is aimed at communism, socialism, everything that differs from the political and economic system of the country. How can anyone bring them any new ideas if they refuse to see anything besides television screens and crime books? When they are not permitted to see anything else?

Here at home we also have numbers of those who want to stop everything, to freeze, to limit. It is not easy to argue with them.

The pictures.

The operating theater. Everyone is around Sasha. Maria Vasilievna with her compassion. Stepa ready to donate his blood. Happy. Petro who had been trying so hard to rehabilitate him. Vasya who wants a dissertation. Irina in the dark laboratory. She loves. Raya also loves. And Sasha himself almost a fanatic of his own formulas into which he writes love, happiness, behavior, society.

Everyone is moved by something in life.

One physiologist (I have forgotten his name) has found the center of pleasure in a rat's brain. He inserted an electrode into it and switched on a low current. Apparently the rat experienced some very pleasurable feeling. No one knows what was in her brain, visions of food, the feeling of giving suck to her children, or meeting with her lover. They had taught her how to switch the current on by pressing the button with her snout. From then on, she forgot everything in the world and spent all her time pressing it. I have even seen a photograph of that lucky rodent.

If only it were possible to introduce such a pleasure wire into the human brain. Then all we should have to do to be happy would be to press the contact, without operations, love, art, books.

The desire to get the maximum pleasure and minimum of the unpleasant, this is the basic mechanism governing our activity. There is a built-in regulator which switches on various programs offered by the body and brain. The brain programs are ingrained by society and supported by creative impulses. Children and animals think only about one day, but adults are trying to look into the future.

The pleasure centers are agitated by the fulfillment of the animal programs, food, love, children. Or simply by the completion of some piece of work. And besides that, by freedom. Gratification of curiosity. Searching. There is also a warm feeling when someone strokes your head, "you're so good." The primitive happiness.

The brain has developed a whole set of conditioned reflexes substituting for these primary agitators of the pleasure centers. These reflexes can become so powerful in man that they can overpower all the bodily signals. Society, people can make them unstoppable. Or at least, give them a powerful stimulus. And once this is started, it often can't be stopped.

Strong agitation of the pleasure center is happiness. It is unfortunate that this soon wears off and is replaced by indifference. It becomes a habit. Lasting animal happiness is impossible, it is too acute. The contrast of suffering makes it even sharper.

With animals it is simpler. You eat your fill, walk around, sleep. A little time, and you are ready again.

It is more difficult with men. The condition agitator, unless it is supported by a basic one, ceases to agitate after a while and may develop into a brake. This is what Pavlov said. Wise words, but they require a small correction. For a dog, yes. Man can develop a set of nonanimal brain agitators which can act continually even when the subject is a completely abstract one. Not without interruptions, of course, but rather like food. Wait a bit and start all over again.

It is good for a man to have such a fixed brain agitator, an urge to invent, to write, to create, to do good to people, or simply to derive happiness out of his work or profession.

Society must teach this to children. To inject into them correct social programs. Otherwise, life may become a disaster. Nature has planted so many traps in our way. Every instinct can be turned into a vice. Food can lead to greed, the sex instinct to lewdness, the desire to receive recognition to egotism and cruel disregard for others.

Is it possible to graft in such nonanimal programs and stop the flow of slush from below?

Well, it is time to go. If this last gamble is lost, then we must again decide what to do next. And there is nothing at all on which a correct decision can be based. Flip a coin? When shall we have those clever machines which could decide for us?

Why worry. I won't live that long. No.

There are so many centrifugal forces separating people. Sasha has defined them clearly in his work. The limitation of learning. Misunderstanding. People don't understand one another simply because they don't know what they are talking about. Semantics. Subjectivity colors everything. One's own convictions discard everything that does not fit them. How much harm has been done by deeply convinced but limited people!

Perhaps the thing which must be done first is the rejection of one's own categorical opinions. We must realize that our own modeling installations are very limited. That all seemingly simple things are in fact complicated and have many sides to them, each as good as another. Multiplicity of truths, each as true as the rest.

And again we need some very intelligent machines able to model and analyze very complicated systems for us. Or at least supply us with material based on definite mathematical facts.

It is easy to write recipes for behavior. It is infinitely more difficult to make up these recipes and prescriptions.

I am going.

Probably everything is ready there.

Must be.

9
MYSELF

THE OPERATING THEATER AGAIN. How many times today?

The situation:

Sasha is on the table. Asleep. He is breathing on his own, through a tube. Lenya is helping him a little, softly squeezing the oxygen bag in rhythm with his own breath. Besides Sasha, on another table, lies our hero Stepa, a blissful smile on his face. Paying in full for his sins and omissions. Between them there is a small table on which is the uncomplicated apparatus for direct blood transfusion. Oleg is in command, ready to start. His face registers impatience. The tube has already been connected to two veins. Marina stands over sterilized instruments on her table.

Oxana is sitting in front of the monitor screen, just as before. She must be very tired. She has been sitting like this for fourteen hours. She is afraid to leave; what if there is another stoppage? The moment we are through with this little operation, I must send her home.

Dima is writing something in his journal. Genya is crouching in front of the drainage tube, counting the drops. Maria Vasilievna is here, Petro, and some of the other youngsters.

Again the same often repeated question:

"What are the showings?"

Dima:

"Everything's normal. We are ready, all the analyses have been taken. We were just going to send for you."

"Very well, Oleg, let's go. Pump steadily without interruptions so that the blood won't coagulate in transit. About one full syringe every twenty seconds."

Oleg goes to work.

"Genya, how's the blood flow?"

"Fluctuating between forty-five and fifty-five drops per minute."

Silence. All I can hear are the small clicks of the apparatus being switched from suction to injection. Dima keeps his hand on Sasha's pulse. Oxana is watching the cardiograph screen without taking her eyes off it for a second.

"Shall we give him additional anesthesia?"

"No, there's no point. There are no shivers."

Five minutes pass. We have transfused some two hundred and fifty milligrams. The hemorrhage rate remains unchanged. Is it possible that this will also prove to be a vain hope?

Well, what shall we do then? Wait longer or open the wound and look for the bleeding vessel? Everything has been considered carefully. Kidneys. Liver. Enough!

"What about urine?"

Genya looks at the bottle connected to the catheter. It is half filled with dark-brown liquid.

"Forty cubes in the last thirty minutes."

Dima cuts in:

"The analyses are slightly improving."

Well, this is not too bad. The kidneys are working. It means that we can go on with the transfusion. I am scared to death of operating again. Let's wait. It is too early to despair.

Oleg is continuing the transfusion. Everything is proceeding smoothly. Stepan looks fine. He is strong, five hundred cubes mean nothing to him. He is tired, hasn't slept for probably forty hours. Can this harm the patient? I remember reading somewhere that dogs receiving tired blood go to sleep. Well, this wouldn't be so bad in our case. The longer Sasha sleeps the better. Let's wait and see.

Everything is going on so simply and undramatically. A newspaperman would call this "heroic sacrifice of a young physician."

"Professor. Two syringes more and we'll have five hundred cubes. Shall I stop?"

Stepan cuts in without waiting for me:

"Take two hundred more, Oleg. I feel fine, it won't hurt me."

"Shut up, Stepa! You won't be a hero to us even if we bleed you to death!"

A hint at our lack of appreciation?

"Let's do it this way: take two hundred and fifty cubes more from Stepan, and immediately give him a plasma transfusion. In this way Sasha will receive all he needs, and Stepan will get a good compensation."

This suggestion comes from Maria Vasilievna. A very wise one. To take seven hundred and fifty cubic milligrams of the donor's blood may be dangerous, but this way the loss will be compensated in full. And of course Stepan's fresh blood is infinitely more beneficial to Sasha than the frozen. They have already given him over a liter of that, and it hasn't produced any results.

The venous pressure is low, and there is no danger of overloading the heart.

"Well Stepa, do you feel dizzy?"

"I? Not at all! I feel fine!"

"All right then, let's do it. There is some ten-day blood in the refrigerator. Get it, and get everything ready for the transfusion, into the same vein. Don't hurry Oleg, let them get ready. Incidentally, how's Onipko? Who has checked on him tonight?"

Petro reports that Onipko is all right.

Maria Vasilievna smiles:

"Stepan owes us a full liter for him."

Meanwhile our hero suddenly begins to wilt. His eyelids droop. He tries to fight drowsiness, but then surrenders and goes to sleep. He even begins to snore a little. We all become slightly alarmed. Dima grabs his wrist, I take the other. This is all we need, another complication. But no. The pulse is good.

"Let's take his blood pressure. I think he's simply tired and of course there's a loss of blood . . . Is his transfusion ready? Don't wake him up, let him sleep through it."

About fifteen minutes have passed since the beginning of the transfusion. On the tenth minute the hemorrhaging seemed to diminish. Nothing conclusive yet.

Meanwhile, the transfusion gear for Stepan has been set up. Oleg takes the last syringe from him, and switches the pump off. Now Stepan begins to get his compensation drop by drop.

"Look at him, sleeps like a saint. Has rehabilitated himself in the eyes of the Chief and the collective!"

To a certain extent, yes. But not completely. He has

proved to us that he is a good man, but will he make a good physician? Only the future will tell. But of course any thought of dismissing him is out of the question for the moment.

"When you finish the transfusion, wheel him into the next room and let him sleep there the whole night if he wants. But keep an eye on him. Anything may happen you know. This is a lot of blood to take out of a tired man."

Now all our attention is concentrated on the blood drainage tube. Everyone is here; several people are counting the drops at the same time. The effect must become evident in ten to fifteen minutes. That is the critical time. If the hemorrhage rate does not improve by then, we shall have to operate. I am in despair when I think about it.

"For the last five minutes the rate hasn't exceeded forty drops."

"Keep counting. Lenya, cut off all anesthesia. Stepan's blood will keep him asleep anyway."

Suddenly there is the click of Genya's stopwatch.

"Thirty drops! This is the lowest yet!"

"We had twenty once. Stop celebrating."

Genya starts his watch again.

"I haven't seen that! While I've been watching it's never gone below forty!"

Everyone is dead tired. At the end of his tether. But we must wait.

Someone wails like a medieval conjurer:

"Stop, stop! Come on, stop, stop!"

But this bit of witchcraft doesn't help. The drops continue to slide down the tube.

"We should have brought in a village bloodstopper.

There used to be old women like that, they would whisper something over the wound, and no more bleeding. My mother saw one herself. True, I don't quite trust Mamma, she's the nervous type."

This is Oleg. Everyone is smiling.

"If we could have found such a home-grown witch we should have signed her up at the clinic at a senior science worker's rate!"

"What rate? We should have all chipped in and paid her double!"

Various joking proposals. Hemorrhaging is one of our principal enemies. One would pay anything to eliminate it. Even out of the eighty-ruble-per-month pay.

Meanwhile Sasha begins to stir. He is waking up.

"Sasha!"

He opens his eyes. Still no recognition in his look.

"Sasha, look at me!"

A few movements of eyelids and brows and then his eyes focus on my face. He has recognized me! I can see this by some undefinable little signs. He moves his head trying to tell me how uncomfortable he feels.

"I know, the tube is bothering you? Wait a little while and we'll take it out."

Yes, we can extract the tube now, but first we must make absolutely sure that his breathing has been fully restored. It seems to me that it has.

"Lie quietly and try to breathe deeply . . . Concentrate on this one program."

Sasha closes his eyes, tries to concentrate, if this is at all possible in his condition. Probably he simply drops off to sleep. The brain has quickly exhausted itself and has switched off.

"Genya, how many drops?"

"Twenty-five for the past three minutes."

Is it possible that our ordeal is coming to an end? Hard to believe. Instinctively I steel myself against new surprises. But logic and experience tell me that the probability of any new complication is not high. For tonight at least. Even the urine is passing well. If the heart continues to work like this, the kidneys will solve their problem.

If only the hemorrhage could be held down. Even if it continues at this rate, this is now not very dangerous. It would stop certainly within twelve hours. The total loss of blood would not be more than six hundred cubes. And that is tolerable.

We are waiting. Ten minutes more. We go out to the outside hall to smoke. We don't want to talk any more. It is past midnight.

We come back. Sasha is lying with his eyes open, and they show that he is conscious. He moves his head impatiently. It is obvious that the breathing tube causes him acute discomfort.

"All right, Dima. Let's take it out."

Dima inserts into the trachea a stiff dose of penicillin solution, and then pumps it out through a thin tube. Sasha coughs. This is a good sign. Two tears appear in the corners of his eyes and roll down. Why? Because of coughing, or because of pain?

Dima extracts the packed bandage from the oral cavity. He must have packed it in really tight. Sasha's face instantly assumes its normal expression. Now he can be shown to anyone. Even Irina. This can be done through the glass ceiling while he is still here. However I don't want to go now. Sasha is moving and trying to push out the tube with his tongue.

"All right, all right, keep still. I'm taking it out."

The tube is extracted. This ends the first postoperative stage officially. All the main bodily functions have been restored.

"Well, Sasha, do you think you can say at least one little word to us?"

He makes an effort, smiles and whispers:

"Thanks."

How wonderful it is for all of us to hear this first word!

Not because he thanks us. We are grateful to him for being alive. We all have put our hand to this.

Apparently he has liked the idea of talking. He whispers again, only with his lips:

"Did you put in the valve?"

"Yes, yes, we did. It's sitting very pretty."

He sighs, with immense relief. Apparently he has been thinking about this ever since he came to and has been tortured by doubts. He wanted a new valve, not a plastic patch-up.

"Say something aloud, with full voice."

He winces and then says in a very weak hoarse voice:

"My back hurts, the table is so hard."

"We'll transfer you into a bed straightaway."

Of course his back hurts! We took him out of the ward at ten in the morning and now it is almost one o'clock, fifteen hours. But now this is all. Two ward nurses are wheeling in the bed. The rollers creak; as always, they have not been properly oiled. But who cares?

"Take all analyses for the last time, and let's move him into the ward."

There is no point in keeping him in the postanesthesia room. We can do everything in the ward.

I'm glad. Very glad. Nonetheless I think I'll go and let Irina look at him through the glass. They will admit Raya into the ward, but it may be a long time before this poor Irina will see him again. Perhaps a very long time.

And maybe even never. This also is still possible.

I run up to the third floor, knock at the laboratory door. She opens it at once, frightened:

"Something's wrong?"

"On the contrary, everything's fine. Come with me, I'll show him to you through the ceiling glass, while he's still in the theater."

I walk with her quickly to the observation room. Fortunately it is deserted.

It is a strange picture from here. Somewhat unreal. You can't hear voices. People are walking under your feet just like a silent film.

Sasha has already been moved into the bed. They are fixing the holders for transfusion drips. Maria Vasilievna is wiping his forehead with a wet towel. She is doing this in a special surgical way, lightly and yet thoroughly. I know this from experience, no one can wipe sweat off my face during operations like Masha.

Irina presses her face against the glass, probably wants him to notice her. But it is not necessary, really. He shouldn't be emotionally disturbed for the moment. Sleep would be the best thing for him. But he is awake.

I gently touch her arm. "Well, that's enough, dear. Stop it. Come into my room for a moment."

"Professor, please. A second more."

I am waiting impatiently near the door. A reflexive

thought: Poor girl. But only for an instant, now I'm an optimist. Everything will work out. Sasha is alive, and that's the main thing.

I see the bed being wheeled out. Irina rises and joins me, walking behind me.

We come to my room. I don't want any long conversations. Dismissing politeness, I remain standing not offering her a chair.

"Irina Nikolayevna, this is all for tonight. Now you must go home."

She makes a protesting move, but I cut her off: "Please, no arguments! Nothing will happen until tomorrow. Leave your telephone number. I shall sleep here."

"Well, I suppose I must obey. I have no rights . . . even to go behind the coffin."

I have absolutely no desire to engage in any emotional discussions. I don't want to complicate my life for the moment. Therefore let her go. Later. Later we'll sort all this out.

"Let's go. I'll walk with you to the door. The main entrance is closed."

"You don't have to. I've been here before, at night."

Is that so? Very strange. I thought they hadn't been seeing each other here. All right, I won't go into details. If she's been here, she's been here. Probably while he was here the last time.

"Thank you very much, Professor. I hope you will find time to speak to me, one of these days?"

"Yes, of course. I'll telephone you, or you'll telephone me. You can call me at home."

"Goodbye then. Please, look after Sasha, will you?"

Why does she say that? But then, she's in love, and

this is stronger than friendship. Therefore she has the right to talk this way.

She leaves. Good. Another problem has been put behind. At least for the time being. I shall go to the ward, they must have taken him there by now. Could something have happened in transit? It seems to be so easy, to wheel a patient into the lift and out of it, but some patients react even to that.

I am walking along a long corridor. Overhead lights have been switched off; only here and there night lamps on nurses' posts cast their glow upon their desks. Everything is quiet and peaceful. No one moans. On this floor are mostly children with congenital heart disorders. All wards have glass doors. Everything is dark. No, here is some light. What does this mean? Shall I look in?

A small room, three beds. Two girls are asleep, their blankets are disarranged. One of them, Lusya, has been operated on and will be sent home in a few days. Petro sewed up a hole between the ventricles using the blood-circulation machine. There were postoperative complications, and we have had quite a bit of trouble with her. Once we sat around her bed the whole night. But now she is asleep, so pink and pretty. Smiling. Dreaming about coming home and seeing her dolls again? She is happy. She looks a little like my Lenochka.

Nothing alarming has happened here. Anna Maximovna, the fat middle-aged nurse, is giving a penicillin injection to Vitya. The boy is half asleep and whimpering. She is talking to him softly and tenderly. This is pleasant to hear.

The postoperative station. Maria Dmitrievna is fumbling with some syringes. Why is she here? Has she not been relieved? No, Sonya is here.

"Maria Dmitrievna, what are you doing here?"

"Oh, I got stuck a little and then the last bus left and it was too late to go home."

This is a barefaced lie. I know that she lives two blocks away from the clinic. She simply did not want to let some less experienced nurse take care of Sasha. She knows that this is going to be a difficult night for him.

I walk into the ward. Sasha is in bed, his eyes are closed. He is moaning softly. Pain. The first night is always difficult. You can't use too much sedation, because it inhibits breathing, and smaller doses don't produce any effect. But he is pink. This is good.

Doctors and nurses are all around him. Dima is taking his blood pressure, Lenya is writing something in the chart, Genya is again near the drainage tube. Oxana is rigging up her cardioscope; she probably wants to check on the heart action here in the ward before leaving.

Even Valya is here with her test tubes. Petro, Oleg, the whole crowd. They won't let him die. If this could be done always.

"No problems in transit?"

"The blood pressure has gone down a little, but it's rising."

"Well, Sasha, how is it?"

He opens his eyes. The look of a suffering man. He probably thinks, "It would be better to die."

"Keep it up, Sasha. It will be easier tomorrow. Use your will power."

He whispers:

"I'll try, thanks."

"Hold back your thanks a little. Much depends on you now. Remember the influence of the brain on the whole structure. And now, just try to sleep and let us worry."

Maria Vasilievna comes in with Raya. Raya's face is pale, tired, wet with tears. A crumpled handkerchief is in her hand.

She comes to me, finds my hand, squeezes it.

"I've been suffering so much, so much."

She has been suffering! And what about all the others? And Sasha! But probably she doesn't mean it that way. I won't tell her anything unpleasant.

"Never mind, Raissa Sergeyevna, the worst is over. Just look at him, and go away, he needs rest. If you don't want to go home, we'll arrange a bed for you in the interns' room on the first floor."

"I'd like to stay with him. Please!"

"Out of the question! Don't even ask. We don't allow anyone to stay in the wards, not even in the children's!"

I won't let her stay here. One can't expect anything from her besides panic. Let her look and get out.

Sasha hears her voice, I hoped he wouldn't. But he crooks his finger, gestures to her to come closer. Whispers:

"Raya, how's Serezha?"

"Everything's fine, darling, don't worry. I have telephoned home. He doesn't know anything."

"Don't tell him—before we know for sure."

It means that he is still conscious of danger. He has been in this clinic too long not to realize that anything might happen. I can imagine how he longs to see his son, after having faced death. Never mind, my friend. Now I have hope. The valve is a pretty good thing. If it is inserted well, it can work like a clock. For months;

perhaps, for years. And later, well, we'll think about that later.

"Oxana, what's with you?"

"A hundred and seventeen. The arrhythmia just as before, no better, no worse, but the function of the myocardium seems to be improving."

To Genya:

"How many drops?"

"Twenty, and steady. No indication of increasing. And the liquid has become more transparent."

That's good. This danger is over. I look at the urine bottle. It is also filling up well.

"Oxana, wrap up and go home. Leave the screen here. They will watch it."

To others:

"Well, Comrades, this is all for tonight. Tomorrow is another day. One surgeon and one anesthetist will stay here overnight. Maria, put up Raissa Sergeyevna for the night."

And so, the day is done. It seems that Sasha will not die tonight. I can sleep for a while. I can't go home though, in case something happens. Medicine is not a precise science. I shall ask Aunt Fenya to make a bed for me in my office. A cup of tea would have been nice, but that's improbable. The kitchen is closed, and the nurses wouldn't have any. Or would they?

I find Fenya, our night nanny, tell her the problem. She considers it.

A fine old woman. How many of our former patients remember you with a warm feeling! And how many eyes have you closed!

"I'll speak to the head nurse, see what I can do. Don't worry, we'll think up something."

I'm not worrying. I can do without tea.

Once again I'm in my office. Dammit, how tired I am of this room.

Let's open the window. Moist darkness. It is drizzling outside. This is very good for the young buds. How wonderfully they smell, those first linden buds! I can never have enough of that fragrance.

Let's have a cigarette. The last one for tonight.

Victory. Victory over death. Sounds a little pompous. I don't like theatrical phrases like that, but they always come into my head, driven there by books, newspapers, radio.

Am I glad? Of course! Sasha is alive. He will think, talk, write. I can see him sitting in that chair there, developing his theories. Sparkling eyes. Broad gestures.

Stop! Don't let your fantasy run wild. There are many unpleasant possibilities yet. Very well, I won't.

I'm glad, but still I do not feel the happy excitement which I used to feel when I was young. I'm tired. So this battle has been won, perhaps. (Touch wood! Funny.) Well, almost won. This is pleasant. Very. And still I feel that another layer of something dark and painful has been deposited in my soul. I can't explain it. Probably, the residue of fear and pain. I've had enough of both today.

A picture: the blood spurting furiously from the hole in the ventricle. I am tied in knots by fear and despair. Nothing is left inside me but this terror, while some of my brain centers are working furiously trying to cope with the situation. Well, I won. But it could have been different. An enormous loss of blood, the heart is empty. Massage. Weak, infrequent contractions. Within me everything is crying: "Contract, contract, for God's sake, contract!" Now it begins to stop, and finally becomes still. Nothing else can be done. Everyone lets his arms fall. I stand for a moment, understanding nothing. Then go away. "Stitch it up." Emptiness. I am envying him. I wish I were dead.

And another: Dima is standing on the stool savagely pressing on Sasha's chest. Sweat is running down his face, his eyes are full of fear. Oxana is dashing round her screen, wringing her hands. A quick thought: Well, this is it; even if it starts again, it will stop. I can do nothing, I just watch. And cry inside. Anger, anger at everyone. "Missed again, you bastards!" Other epithets, even saltier. And what about yourself? Who was sitting there upstairs reading cybernetics? A new wave of savage anger, at myself, at medicine. Oxana's voice: "No contractions!" "All right, stop, you—" Everyone is standing about, motionless, crushed.

All right, let's not imagine things. This time it was different. All has gone well—more or less well. The burden has been lifted, like a saddle from a horse, but the sores remain, the ache.

These sores deposited in my soul over a period of so many years don't permit me to feel any jubilation now. Or ever.

Then abandon it all! You can find some easy work—deliver lectures to students, operate on hernias, sometimes a bit of abdominal surgery, gall bladders. There will be also some unpleasant moments, but nothing like *this,* once I turn difficult cases over to young doctors to experiment on. You can help Lenochka to do her homework, read good books, go to the theater. Even think up various theories of medicine and write books. Comfort, bliss. And the same money, or more. Money is a secondary consideration. Not altogether, but what I have is enough.

Aunt Fenya brings in some tea! Two glasses, a few slices of white bread. And even on a clean towel!

"Please eat, Comrade Professor. You are probably tired after a day like this."

"Thank you, Aunt Fenya, thank you very much."

The old woman would like to stay here and chat, but somehow I don't know how to carry on such conversations. She understood from my expression that I'd like to be alone and went out, promising to bring in some bedding.

How wonderful it is to drink hot tea when your entire mouth is coated with tobacco! I suppose I could eat something more substantial now. Well, never mind.

I am tired. My back is aching. A heavy head. And still I know that I won't sleep. Overwork. Sedatives? I'd better wait. I must try to keep myself in check.

They should give Sasha some sleeping pills. Probably Dima will take care of that. Shall I go and take another look? I can't force myself to get up. Dima will not forget.

The meaning of life. To save people, to perform complicated operations. To work on new and better ones, so that fewer people would die. To teach young doctors to work honestly. Science, theories. To understand my work and do it better. This is my craft. This is the way I serve others. My duty.

Now something else: Lenochka. Everyone must rear children. This is not only a duty, but a necessity. This is pleasant. Very.

And now something personal. To understand what this is all about. Why treat people, educate children, when the world stands on the brink of destruction? Perhaps all that I'm trying to do is already senseless. I want to believe very much that this is not so. But belief is not enough. I want to know. I want to touch those calculations which affect our future.

Nonetheless, it is wonderful that Sasha is alive! True, I don't think he'll live long enough to see his thinking machines. But he will contribute something to this work. If only that Irina lets him. A family breakup, divorce, emotions. He wouldn't live through them. But how to guard him against it? I will try, of course, but my means are limited. His brain is a system which I can't run. Besides, he's much more intelligent than I. I just hope I can save his heart, the physical one, without trying to save his soul. (Soul! Ridiculous.) Never mind. If necessary, I'll put in another valve. Or even an entire artificial heart. They are working on that.

How brave you are! Do you know how many valves you yourself are good for? One scientist said that each person has just so much of adaptable energy given to him at birth, to handle and resist all the strong outside influences. Almost surely I have pretty nearly spent my quota. But maybe that scientist was mistaken? Well, never mind, I'll keep spending it for as long as I can, without trying to economize. I want to be useful to humanity. I am admiring myself again. What a hero!

It is disgusting to catch yourself doing this. "I am giving so much of myself to my patients! I am fighting so selflessly against death!" A hell of a thing. Does this happen to me only, or to other people as well?

Man. First of all, every man must do something, well,

poorly or just average. He must also think about his work. Also differently, deeply or superficially, but he must do it. Third, he must learn to examine his work and his thoughts in a detached way. This is a good medicine for some diseases—for instance, vanity. One can step out of oneself and look at oneself objectively. And then, in most cases, he will discover that he is neither good nor bad, but just average.

Where is Aunt Fenya with those blankets? Perhaps she is delicately giving me time to finish my tea, knowing that if I see a bed I should collapse into it without eating. But most probably she is just giving a bedpan to some patient. Good.

I see her coming, and she is dragging a mattress with her!

"Aunt Fenya, what for? This divan is very soft."

"I want you to be comfortable, Professor. You look pretty awful."

"How are things in the postoperative station? Have you heard anything?"

"Everything must be pretty quiet, Comrade Professor. Maria Dmitrievna went to the head nurse's room to lie down for a while, she wouldn't have done it if there were anything. She specially stayed here to take care of Sasha. But he must be all right. You have golden hands."

"Stop it! You needn't praise me too!"

"And how not to praise you? Everyone is saying the same thing, the whole town—"

"All right, all right."

Meaning: Please go away, granny. I don't know whether she understood or not, but she leaves, wishing me goodnight.

There's not much of the night left. It is now one-thirty, and I never sleep later than six.

I undress, switch off the desk lamp and stretch out. What a delight, to lie down after a day like this! My whole body is aching. However, this is a pleasant ache. The sheets are not too well ironed. I can feel it with my skin. Our laundry is not working too well. To hell with it!

Sleep, sleep, sleep.

I am lying still. The process of relaxation must spread from the motor centers to the brain.

But somehow it doesn't.

Sleep . . . sleep . . .

No, the machine is working. Again, about the meaning of life. There is no meaning: just two sets of behavior programs. This, according to Sasha. I have really got used to his ideas. I can juggle them any way I want.

The animal program, to bear children and bring them up. So that they can live and bear their own children. Generally, not a bad program. But it does not imply any specially humane attitude toward one's neighbors. Grab, tear, strike everyone down. To bear good children one must be strong and healthy. Also, this affords secondary pleasures, the sense of conquest, domination, material self-enrichment. The brain gives these animal pleasures some added taste.

Faces, events . . . drifting through my mind. Some animal programs . . . To brag about my valve operation in the Society, one of them. Crying Raya, another one. Has Irina reached her home yet? She loves Sasha, the third animal program.

Second programs, the social ones. Man must work for others. Even when this is unpleasant. So that everyone can live better. This doesn't bring such sharp pleasures as love and children. Sometimes, no pleasure at all. But one must force himself.

It was simpler before. People believed in God. Love your neighbor, go to paradise. Otherwise, the eternal fire. Punishment and encouragement, based on the selfsame animal programs.

There is no God. Science. Everyone knows: the punishment can come only from men, here and now. If you are crafty and clever, you can avoid it. And derive pleasure from living. The triumph of instincts. Freudianism.

And what about happiness?

The primitive man was happy when he had enough food, when he was warm and with his family. And the modern one? He can't live without society. He gets pleasure out of communion not only with his dear ones, but with strangers, pleasure from his work, out of doing something which is appreciated by others; all this has become necessary for his spiritual comfort.

There is a rather overworked expression, "useful social activity." One shouldn't laugh at it. Happiness coming from below is sharp, but it is not lasting, and is not sufficient to sustain the modern man. Only when it is combined with this useful social activity does it provide man with a secure anchor in life.

But, my friend, who is arguing against that? Have you ever read anything anywhere to contradict this? In books, in newspapers, no; but some people do not follow this rule. Then you must argue with them, prove to them this self-evident truth.

And what about yourself?

I have lived long enough. My animal emotions have

gone to the second place. I don't want anything which they bring, I know there is no sense in that. I am not fooling myself. The instinct of survival keeps me living, but it doesn't give me happiness.

Then what really sustains me? Family, Lenochka. Yes, of course, but that isn't enough. When on a holiday with the family, I go crazy. I don't know what to do with myself. What then? Little faces of the children when they go home from the clinic? Their mothers' eyes?

I realize that all these social programs are artificially grafted into me by society. Very well! I don't care. They give me satisfaction and help me to bear all difficulties.

Probably it is very essential to convince yourself that this is so. Once you're convinced, you're happy. So I am happy, so what?

Sleep, you happy one. Sleep.

No, to fall asleep is not that easy. New thoughts march into the brain, rank after rank. Today has already gone by. Sasha will live, almost certainly. One more valve successfully put in. This is important, this is another valve. Every day luckless people come to us with mitral insufficiencies. We used to shrug our shoulders, and send them away. Now all this is in the past.

If we perform just one operation per week, many people can be saved. But it is possible to perform even two. Like the one we had today? No, that's too much. All my girls and boys were completely exhausted, and will take days to recover. Myself, also. But we shall improve our technique. Perhaps Genya's idea about inserting valves is really a breakthrough. Clever boy. Does he ever think about the meaning of life? Probably not yet. But he is kind, and that is sufficient meaning for him.

All right, if we put in just one valve per week, we can operate on about forty cases a year. This is already a figure about which one can talk. Figure? Talk? Those animal programs are indestructible. Well, to hell with them. I am what I am. Too late to become a saint.

What surgery do we have booked for tomorrow? The operation with the AIK machine has been called off. It is too bad I have surrendered to weakness. Perhaps we can still go ahead with it? No. They have already told the boy's mother. A mother's heart is not a toy, you can't bounce it back and forth. So, instead of that little Lenya, we'll take that man, Sorokin, with the constricted aorta. Petro will do the actual surgery. Yes, that's a good idea. But if I remember correctly, there are possible lime deposits in the valve there. So I'll have to stand by and take over if it becomes necessary.

Yes, but I wanted to leave early tomorrow and do some writing. I should have sent that article long ago. Never mind, it can wait. Wait. It is good to get tired, and then stretch out like this. If only not tomorrow . . . with its worries . . . always more worries . . .